PU

Edito

THE MERI

An unrivalled collecti— —erse – poems, folk rhymes and songs, carols, nonsense songs, story poems, lyrics and ballads – each one especially chosen to give delight, whether it is an old favourite or something completely new and unusual. Poems to make you laugh, riddles to guess, songs to sing, the very best from every kind of poetry, arranged here in a lively sequence with nothing dull or dreary to spoil the sparkling whole.

There are poems for six-year-olds, and many for twelve-year-olds; most readers over nine will love them all.

This Puffin edition contains a few less than the 400 poems of the original edition. Most of the other poems you can already find in the other Puffin poetry books.

Cover design by Gunvor Edwards

Illustrations by *John Mackay*

A collection of rhymes and poems

THE MERRY·GO··ROUND

Chosen by James Reeves

Puffin Books

Puffin Books: a Division of Penguin Books Ltd,
Harmondsworth, Middlesex, England
Penguin Books Inc., 7110 Ambassador Road, Baltimore, Maryland 21207, U.S.A.
Penguin Books Australia Ltd, Ringwood, Victoria, Australia
Penguin Books Canada Ltd, 41 Steelcase Road West, Markham, Ontario, Canada
Penguin Books (N.Z.) Ltd, 182-190 Wairau Road, Auckland 10, New Zealand

—

This collection first published by Heinemann Educational Books 1955
Published, slightly abridged, in Puffin Books 1967
Reprinted 1969, 1971, 1973, 1974

—

Made and printed in Great Britain by
Cox & Wyman Ltd,
London, Reading and Fakenham
Set in Monotype Imprint

CONTENTS

HERE is a new collection of verse for children of all ages. It is arranged in four parts. The simplest rhymes and poems, suitable for the youngest readers of all, are contained in the first part; the poems intended mainly for older children are in the fourth part. For this Puffin edition, the text has been slightly abridged, to avoid in particular repetition of poems already published in Puffin books.

ACKNOWLEDGEMENTS

THE editor and publishers gratefully acknowledge the permission of the following to include copyright poems in this book:

The Literary Trustees of Walter de la Mare and the Society of Authors as their representative, for *Silver*, *No Jewel*, *Quack*, *Sooeep* and *The Old Tailor*; Miss Elena Fearn for *Birds*; the Executor of the late Gordon Bottomley and Professor Colleer Abbott for *Dawn*; the late Hilaire Belloc and Messrs Gerald Duckworth and Co. Ltd for *The Big Baboon*; Mr Robert Graves for *Henry and Mary*, *Six Badgers*, *A Cough*, *The Pumpkin*, *The Penny Fiddle*, *King Stephen*, *Allie* and *Four Children*; Mrs Iris Wise and Messrs Macmillan and Co. Ltd for *The Wood of Flowers* from *Collected Poems* by James Stephens; the Estate of Sir Henry Newbolt for *Rilloby-Rill*, from *Poems Old and New* published by Messrs John Murray; Harcourt Brace and World Inc. for *hist whist*, copyright, 1923, 1951, by E. E. Cummings, reprinted from his volume *Poems 1923–1954*; Mrs W. H. Davies and Messrs Jonathan Cape Ltd for *The Woods and Banks*, *Sheep*, *Nailsworth Hill*, *My Garden*, *In Springtime* and *The Cat*; The Macmillan Company for *The King of Yellow Butterflies* from *The Chinese Nightingale and Other Poems* by Vachel Lindsay, copyright The Macmillan Company 1917, renewed 1945; the Trustees of the Hardy Estate and Macmillan and Co. for *We Be the King's Men* from *The Dynasts* by Thomas Hardy; Messrs Boosey and Hawkes Music Publishers Ltd for *O What if the Fowler* by Charles Dalmon. The text of the Authorized Version of the Bible is Crown copyright, and the extracts used herein are reproduced by permission.

PART ONE

YELLOW WHEELS

BELL HORSES

Bell horses, bell horses,
  What time of day?
One o'clock, two o'clock,
  Three and away

Bell horses, bell horses,
  What time of day?
Three o'clock, four o'clock,
  Five and away

Bell horses, bell horses,
  What time of day?
Five o'clock, six o'clock,
  Time now to stay.

BESSY AND MARY

Bessy Bell and Mary Gray,
  They were two bonny lasses;
They built their house upon the lea
  And covered it with rashes.

Bessy kept the garden gate,
  And Mary kept the pantry:
Bessy always had to wait,
  While Mary lived in plenty.

BETTY AND I

Betty my sister and I fell out.
And what do you think it was all about?
She loved coffee and I loved tea,
And that was the reason we could not agree.

BIRTHDAYS

Monday's child is fair of face,
Tuesday's child is full of grace,
Wednesday's child is full of woe,
Thursday's child has far to go,
Friday's child is loving and giving,
Saturday's child works hard for its living;
But the child who is born on the Sabbath day
Is bonny and blithe and good and gay.

THE BONNY CRAVAT

Jenny, come tie my,
Jenny, come tie my,
Jenny, come tie my bonny cravat.
I've tied it behind,
I've tied it before,
I've tied it so often I'll tie it no more.

BOW-WOW, SAYS THE DOG

Bow-wow, says the dog,
　　Mew-mew, says the cat;
Grunt-grunt, goes the hog;
　　And squeak goes the rat.

Tu-whu, says the owl;
　　Caw-caw, says the crow;
Quack-quack, says the duck;
　　And moo, says the cow.

BUDLEIGH FAIR

Come up, my horse, to Budleigh Fair;
What shall we have when we come there?
Sugar and figs and alicumpane;*
Home again, home again, Master and Dame.

* A sweetmeat.

13

A BUMBLE-BEE

What do I see?
A bumble-bee
Sit on a rose
And wink at me!

What do you mean
By 'Hum, hum, hum'?
If you mean me,
I dare not come!

CALICO PIE

Calico Pie,
The little birds fly
Down to the Calico tree.
Their wings were blue
And they sang 'Tilly-loo' –
Till away they all flew,
   And they never came back to me,
    They never came back,
    They never came back,
   They never came back to me.

EDWARD LEAR

A CAT CAME FIDDLING

A cat came fiddling out of a barn,
With a pair of bag-pipes under her arm,
She could sing nothing but 'Fiddle-de-dee,
The mouse has married the bumble bee.'
Pipe, cat – dance, mouse –
We'll have a wedding at our good house.

THE CAT HAS EATEN THE
PUDDING-STRING

Sing, sing, what shall I sing?
The cat has eaten the pudding-string!
Do, do, what shall I do?
The cat has bitten it quite in two.

A CHERRY

As I went through the garden gap,
Who should I meet but Dick Red-cap!
A stick in his hand, a stone in his throat.
If you'll tell me this riddle, I'll give you a groat.

COCK-A-DOODLE-DOO!

Cock-a-doodle-doo!
My dame has lost her shoe;
My master's lost his fiddle-stick,
And don't know what to do.

Cock-a-doodle-doo!
My dame has found her shoe,
And master's found his fiddle-stick,
Cock-a-doodle-doo!

Cock-a-doodle-doo!
My dame shall dance with you,
My master's found his fiddle-stick,
Cock-a-doodle-doo!

CORPORAL TIM

Corporal Tim
Was dressed so trim,
He thought them all afraid of him;
But sad to say,
The very first day
We had a fight,
He died of fright,
And that was the end of Corporal Tim.

CURLYLOCKS

Curlylocks, Curlylocks,
    Wilt thou be mine?
Thou shalt not wash dishes,
    Nor yet feed the swine;
But sit on a cushion,
    And sew a fine seam,
And feed upon strawberries,
    Sugar and cream.

DANCE TO YOUR DADDY

Dance to your Daddy,
    My bonny laddie,
Dance to your Daddy, my bonny lamb!
    You shall get a fishie
    On a little dishie,
You shall get a herring when the boat comes hame!

Dance to your Daddy,
    My bonny laddie,
Dance to your Daddy, and to your Mammie sing!
    You shall get a coatie
    And a pair of breeches,
You shall get a coatie when the boat comes in.

DILLY DILLY

'O, what have you got for dinner, Mrs Bond?'
'There's beef in the larder, and ducks in the pond,
   Crying Dilly, dilly, dilly, dilly, come to be killed;
   For you must be stuffed, and my customers filled.'

'John Ostler, go fetch me a duckling or two,
John Ostler, go fetch me a duckling or two,
   Cry Dilly, dilly, dilly, dilly, come to be killed;
   For you must be stuffed, and my customers filled.'

'I have been to the ducks that are swimming in the pond,
And they won't come to be killed, Mrs Bond:
   I cried Dilly, dilly, dilly, dilly, come to be killed;
   For you must be stuffed, and my customers filled.'

Mrs Bond she went down to the pond in a rage,
With her apron full of onions and her pockets full of sage.
   She cried 'Come, little wagtails, come to be killed;
   For you shall be stuffed, and my customers filled.'

THE DUSTY MILLER

Oh, the little rusty, dusty, rusty miller!
I'll not change my wife for either gold or siller.

DON'T CARE

Don't Care didn't care,
    Don't care was wild:
Don't Care stole plum and pear
    Like any beggar's child.

Don't Care was made to care,
    Don't Care was hung:
Don't Care was put in a pot
    And boiled till he was done.

EIGHT O'CLOCK

Eight o'clock;
The postman's knock!
Five letters for Papa;
    One for Lou,
    And none for you,
And three for dear Mamma.

CHRISTINA ROSSETTI

THE FIFTH OF NOVEMBER

Please to remember the fifth of November,
    Gunpowder, treason, and plot;
I see no reason why gunpowder treason
    Should ever be forgot.

THE FARMYARD

Up was I on my father's farm
  On a May day morning early,
Feeding of my father's sheep
  On a May day morning early.
    With a baa baa here and a baa baa there
    Here a baa, there a baa,
      Here a pretty baa!
Six pretty maids come again along with me
  To the merry green fields and the farmyard.

Up was I on my father's farm
  On a May day morning early,
Feeding of my father's cows
  On a May day morning early.
    With a moo moo here and a moo moo there,
    Here a moo, there a moo,
      Here a pretty moo!
Six pretty maids come again along with me
  To the merry green fields and the farmyard.

Up was I on my father's farm
  On a May day morning early,
Feeding of my father's hens
  On a May day morning early.
    With a cluck cluck here, and a cluck cluck there,
    Here a cluck, there a cluck,
      Here a pretty cluck!
Six pretty maids come again along with me
  To the merry green fields and the farmyard.

Up was I on my father's farm
　On a May day morning early,
Feeding of my father's ducks
　On a May day morning early.
　　With a quack quack here, and a quack quack
　　　there,
　　Here a quack, there a quack,
　　　Here a pretty quack!
Six pretty maids come again along with me
　To the merry green fields and the farmyard.

FINIKY HAWKES

Here's Finiky Hawkes,
As busy as any,
Will well black your shoes,
And charge but a penny.

THE FLY AND THE
BUMBLE-BEE

Fiddle-de-dee, fiddle-de-dee,
The fly hath married the bumble-bee.
And all the birds of the air did sing,
'Have you ever seen so strange a thing?
Fiddle-de-dee, fiddle-de-dee,
The fly hath married the bumble-bee.'

FLY AWAY, PETER

Two little blackbirds sitting on a wall,
One named Peter, the other named Paul.
Fly away, Peter, fly away, Paul –
Come back, Peter, come back, Paul!

FOUR-AND-TWENTY TAILORS

Four-and-twenty tailors
    Went to catch a snail.
Even the bravest of them
    Dared not touch her tail.
She stuck out her horns
    Like a little Kyloe cow
Run, tailors, run,
    Or she'll have you all now!

A FROG HE WOULD
A-WOOING GO

A frog he would a-wooing go,
  Heigh ho, says Rowley,
Whether his mother would let him or no.
  With a roly-poly, gammon and spinach,
  Heigh-ho, says Anthony Rowley!

So off he set with his opera hat,
  Heigh-ho, says Rowley,
And on the road he met with a rat.
  With a roly-poly, gammon and spinach,
  Heigh-ho, says Anthony Rowley!

'Pray, Mr Rat, will you go with me,
    Heigh-ho, says Rowley,
Kind Mrs Mousey for to see?'
    With a roly-poly, gammon and spinach,
    Heigh-ho, says Anthony Rowley!

When they came to the door of Mousey's hall,
    Heigh-ho, says Rowley,
They gave a loud knock and they gave a loud call.
    With a roly-poly, gammon and spinach,
    Heigh-ho, says Anthony Rowley!

'Pray, Mrs Mouse, are you within?'
    Heigh-ho, says Rowley,
'Oh yes, kind sirs, I'm sitting to spin.'
    With a roly-poly, gammon and spinach,
    Heigh-ho, says Anthony Rowley!

'Pray, Mrs Mouse, will you give us some beer?
  Heigh-ho, says Rowley,
For Froggy and I are fond of good cheer.'
  With a roly-poly, gammon and Spinach,
  Heigh-ho, says Anthony Rowley!

'Pray, Mr Frog, will you give us a song?
  Heigh-ho, says Rowley,
But let it be something that's not very long.'
  With a roly-poly, gammon and spinach,
  Heigh-ho, says Anthony Rowley!

'Indeed, Mrs Mouse,' replied the frog,
  Heigh-ho, says Rowley,
'A cold has made me as hoarse as a dog.'
  With a roly-poly, gammon and spinach,
  Heigh-ho, says Anthony Rowley!

'Since you have caught cold, Mr Frog,' Mousey said,
  Heigh-ho, says Rowley,
'I'll sing you a song that I have just made.'
  With a roly-poly, gammon and spinach,
  Heigh-ho, says Anthony Rowley!

But while they were all a merry-making,
  Heigh-ho, says Rowley,
A cat and her kittens came tumbling in,
  With a roly-poly, gammon and spinach,
  Heigh-ho, says Anthony Rowley!

The cat she seized the rat by the crown;
  Heigh-ho, says Rowley,

The kittens they pulled the little mouse down,
  With a roly-poly, gammon and spinach,
  Heigh-ho, says Anthony Rowley!

This put Mr Frog in a terrible fright,
  Heigh-ho, says Rowley,
He took up his hat and he wished them good night,
  With a roly-poly, gammon and spinach,
  Heigh-ho, says Anthony Rowley!

But as Froggy was crossing over a brook,
  Heigh-ho, says Rowley,
A lily-white duck came and gobbled him up,
  With a roly-poly, gammon and spinach,
  Heigh-ho, says Anthony Rowley!

So there was an end of one, two and three,
  Heigh-ho, says Rowley,
The rat, the mouse and the little frog-gee!
  With a roly-poly, gammon and spinach,
  Heigh-ho, says Anthony Rowley!

GALLOP A DREARY DUN

Master I have, and I am his man,
  Gallop a dreary dun;
Master I have, and I am his man,
And I'll get a wife as fast as I can;
With a heighly, gayly, gamberaily,
Higgledy, piggledy, niggledy, giggledy,
  Gallop a dreary dun.

THE GIANT

Fee, fie, fo, fum!
I smell the blood of an English man.
Be he alive, or be he dead,
I'll grind his bones to make my bread.

GIDDY GIRLS, NOISY BOYS

  Giddy girls, noisy boys,
  Come and buy my painted toys;
  Medals made of gingerbread,
  And penny horses white and red.

HANDY SPANDY

Handy Spandy, Jack-a-dandy,
Loved plum-cake and sugar-candy;
He bought some at a grocer's shop,
And out he came, hop, hop, hop.

HIGGLEDY PIGGLEDY

Higgledy piggledy,
Here we lie,
Picked and plucked
And put in a pie!

HERE WE COME A-PIPING

Here we come a-piping
In spring-time and in May;
Green fruit a-ripening,
And winter fled away.
The Queen she sits upon the strand,
Fair as a lily, white as wand;
Seven billows on the sea,
Horses riding fast and free,
And bells beyond the sand.

HOPPING FROG

Hopping frog, hop here and be seen,
   I'll not pelt you with stick or stone:
Your cap is laced and your coat is green;
   Good-bye, we'll let each other alone.

CHRISTINA ROSSETTI

HURT NO LIVING THING

Hurt no living thing;
Ladybird, nor butterfly,
Nor moth with dusty wing,
Nor cricket chirping cheerily,
Nor grasshopper so light of leap,
Nor dancing gnat, nor beetle fat,
Nor harmless worms that creep.

CHRISTINA ROSSETTI

HUSH A BA, BIRDIE

Hush a ba, birdie, croon, croon,
  Hush a ba, birdie, croon.
The sheep are gone to the silver wood,
  And the cows are gone to the broom, broom.
And it's braw milking the kye, kye,
  It's braw milking the kye.
The birds are singing, the bells are ringing,
  And the wild deer come galloping by, by –
And hush a ba, birdie, croon, croon,
  Hush a ba, birdie, croon,
The goats are gone to the mountain hye
  And they'll no be hame till noon, noon.

HUSH-A-BYE, BABY

Hush-a-bye, baby, thy cradle is green.
Thy father's a nobleman, mother's a queen,
Betty's a lady and wears a gold ring,
And Johnny's a drummer and drums for the king.

I HAD A LITTLE HOBBY-HORSE

I had a little hobby-horse,
    And it was dapple grey;
Its head was made of pea-straw,
    Its tail was made of hay.

I sold it to an old woman
    For a copper groat –
And I'll not sing my song again
    Without a new coat.

I SAW A SHIP A-SAILING

I saw a ship a-sailing,
    A-sailing on the sea;
And, oh! it was all laden
    With pretty things for thee!

There were comfits in the cabin,
    And apples in the hold;
The sails were made of silk,
    And the masts were made of gold.

The four-and-twenty sailors
   That stood between the decks,
Were four-and-twenty white mice,
   With chains about their necks.

The captain was a duck,
   With a jacket on his back;
And when the ship began to move,
   The captain said, 'Quack! quack!'

I LOVE SIXPENCE

I love sixpence, pretty little sixpence,
   I love sixpence better than my life.
I spent a penny of it, I spent another,
   And I took fourpence home to my wife.

Oh, my little fourpence, pretty little fourpence,
   I love fourpence better than my life.
I spent a penny of it, I spent another,
   And I took twopence home to my wife.

Oh, my little twopence, my pretty little twopence,
　　I love twopence better than my life.
I spent a penny of it, I spent another,
　　And I took nothing home to my wife.

Oh, my little nothing, my pretty little nothing,
　　What will nothing buy for my wife?
I have nothing, I spend nothing,
　　I love nothing better than my life.

JACKY'S FIDDLE

Jacky, come give me the fiddle,
　　If ever thou mean to thrive.
Nay, I'll not give my fiddle
　　To any man alive.

If I should give my fiddle,
　　They'll think that I'm gone mad,
For many a joyful day
　　My fiddle and I have had.

JACK SPRAT

Jack Sprat could eat no fat,
　　His wife could eat no lean,
So it came to pass between them both
　　They licked the platter clean.
Jack ate all the lean,
　　Joan ate all the fat,
The bone they picked it clean,
　　Then gave it to the cat.

Jack Sprat was wheeling
  His wife by the ditch,
The barrow turned over,
  And in she did pitch;
Says Jack, 'She'll be drowned.'
  But Joan did reply,
'I don't think I shall,
  For the ditch is quite dry.'

Joan Sprat went a-brewing
  A barrel of ale,
She put in some hops,
  That it might not turn stale.
But as for the malt,
  She forgot to put that;
'This is brave sober liquor,'
  Said little Jack Sprat.

JEMMY DAWSON

Brave news is come to town,
    Brave news is carried,
Brave news is come to town! –
    Jemmy Dawson's married.

First he got a porridge-pot,
    Then he bought a ladle,
Then he got a wife and child,
    And then he bought a cradle.

JENNY GRAY

I had a little nobby mare,
    Her name was Jenny Gray,
Her head was made of pease-straw,
    Her tail was made of hay.

She could ramble, she could trot,
She could carry a mustard pot,
Round the town of Woodstock!
Hey, Jenny, away!

JOHN COOK'S MARE

John Cook he had a little grey mare;
    Hee, haw, hum!
Her back stood up, and her bones they were bare;
    Hee, haw, hum!

John Cook was riding up Shooter's Bank,
  Hee, haw, hum!
And there his nag did kick and prank;
  Hee, haw, hum!

John Cook was riding up Shooter's Hill;
  Hee, haw, hum!
His mare fell down and she made her will;
  Hee, haw, hum!

The saddle and bridle are laid on the shelf;
  Hee, haw, hum!
If you want any more you may sing it yourself!
  Hee, haw, hum!

JUST LIKE ME

I went up one pair of stairs.
   Just like me.
I went up two pairs of stairs.
   Just like me.
I went into a room.
   Just like me.
I looked out of a window.
   Just like me.
And there I saw a monkey.
   Just like me.

JUNIPER, JUNIPER

Juniper, Juniper,
   Green in the snow;
Sweetly you smell
   And prickly you grow.

Juniper, Juniper,
   Blue in the fall;
Give me some berries,
   Prickles and all.

LADYBIRD, LADYBIRD

Ladybird, ladybird, fly away home!
Your house is on fire, your children are gone
All except one, and her name is Anne;
She crept under the frying-pan.

LAMBS TO SELL

Young lambs to sell, young lambs to sell!
I never would cry 'Young lambs to sell,'
If I had as much money as I could tell,
I never would cry 'Young lambs to sell.'

LOOBY LOO

Here we go looby loo,
   Here we go looby light,
Here we go looby loo
   All on a Saturday night.

Put your right hand in –
   Put your right hand out,
Shake it a little, a little,
   And turn yourself about.

LITTLE LAD

Little lad, little lad,
Where wast thou born?
Far off in Lancashire
Under a thorn,
Where they sup sour milk
From a ram's horn.

MACARONI

Macaroni's come to town,
    On a speckled pony;
He stuck a feather in his crown,
    And cried out 'Macaroni!'

THE MAN IN THE MOON

The Man in the Moon came tumbling down
    And asked the way to Norwich.
He went by the south and burnt his mouth
    With eating cold pease porridge.

A MERRY HEART

Jog on, jog on, the footpath way,
   And merrily hent* the stile-a:
A merry heart goes all the day,
   Your sad tires in a mile-a.

                WILLIAM SHAKESPEARE

* Leap.

MR EAST

Mr East gave a feast,
Mr North laid the cloth,
Mr West took the best,
Mr South burned his mouth
Eating hot potatoes.

MY DAME HATH A LAME
TAME CRANE

My dame hath a lame tame crane,
My dame hath a crane that is lame.
Pray, gentle Jane,
Let my dame's lame tame crane
Feed and come home again.

THE NOBLE DUKE OF YORK

The noble Duke of York,
  He had ten thousand men;
He marched them up to the top of the hill
  And he marched them down again.

And when they were up, they were up,
  And when they were down, they were down,
And when they were only half-way up
  They were neither up nor down.

A NEEDLE AND THREAD

Old Mother Twitchett had but one eye,
And a long tail which she let fly;
And every time she went over a gap,
She left a bit of her tail in a trap.

NOBODY CARES

Tom tied a kettle to the tail of a cat,
Jill put a stone in the blind man's hat,
Bob threw his grandmother down the stairs –
And they all grew up ugly, and nobody cares.

THE NORTH WIND

The North wind doth blow,
And we shall have snow,
And what will the robin do then, poor thing?
O, he'll go to the barn,
And to keep himself warm
He'll hide his head under his wing, poor thing.

The North wind doth blow,
And we shall have snow,
And what will the swallow do then, poor thing?
O, do you not know
He's gone long ago
To a country much warmer than ours, poor thing?

The North wind doth blow,
And we shall have snow,
And what will the dormouse do then, poor thing?
Rolled up in a ball,
In his nest snug and small,
He'll sleep till the winter is past, poor thing.

The North wind doth blow,
And we shall have snow,
And what will the children do then, poor things?
O, when lessons are done,
They'll jump, skip and run,
And play till they make themselves warm, poor
things.

OLD CHAIRS TO MEND

If I'd as much money as I could spend,
I never would cry 'Old chairs to mend!'
Old chairs to mend, old chairs to mend!
I never would cry 'Old chairs to mend!'

If I'd as much money as I could tell,
I never would cry 'Old clothes to sell!'
Old clothes to sell, old clothes to sell!
I never would cry 'Old clothes to sell!'

THE OLD GREY GOOSE

Go and tell Aunt Nancy,
Go and tell Aunt Nancy,
Go and tell Aunt Nancy,
   The old grey goose is dead.

The one that she was saving,
The one that she was saving,
The one that she was saving,
   To make a feather bed.

She died on Friday,
She died on Friday,
She died on Friday,
   Behind the old barn shed.

She left nine little goslings,
She left nine little goslings,
She left nine little goslings,
   To scratch for their own bread.

OLD LOVELL

Have you seen Old Lovell
With his wooden pick and shovel
   Digging up potatoes in the turnpike road?

Have you seen his wife
With a broad-bladed knife
   Scraping the potatoes in the turnpike road?

Have you seen his daughter
With a pail of dirty water
   Washing the potatoes in the turnpike road?

ONE MISTY MOISTY MORNING

One misty moisty morning,
   When cloudy was the weather,
I met a little old man
   Clothed all in leather,
Clothed all in leather,
   With a strap beneath his chin,
With a how d'ye do and a how d'ye do,
   And a how d'ye do again.
He began to compliment,
   And I began to grin,
With a how d'ye do and a how d'ye do,
   And a how d'ye do again.

SIMON BRODIE

Simon Brodie had a cow;
   He lost his cow and he couldna find her;
When he had done what man could do,
The cow came home and her tail behind her.

ORANGES AND LEMONS

Gay go up and gay go down,
To ring the bells of London town.

Ha'pence and farthings,
Say the bells of St Martin's.

Oranges and lemons,
Say the bells of St Clement's.

Pancakes and fritters,
Say the bells of St Peter's.

Two sticks and an apple,
Say the bells of Whitechapel.

Kettles and pans,
Say the bells of St Anne's.

You owe me ten shillings,
Say the bells of St Helen's.

When will you pay me?
Say the bells of Old Bailey.

When I grow rich,
Say the bells of Shoreditch.

Pray when will that be?
Say the bells of Stepney.

I'm sure I don't know,
Says the great bell of Bow.

PETER AND MICHAEL

Peter and Michael were two little menikin,
They kept a cock and a fat little henikin:
Instead of an egg it laid a gold penikin,
Oh, how they wish it would do it againikin!

THE PIPER'S COW

There was a piper had a cow
  And had no hay to give her,
He played a tune upon his pipes,
  'Consider, old cow, consider!'
That old cow considered well
  And promised her master money
Only to play that other tune,
  'Corn rigs are bonny.'

POP GOES THE WEASEL

Half a pound of twopenny rice,
  Half a pound of treacle;
Stir it up and make it nice,
  Pop goes the weasel!

Up and down the City Road,
  In and out the Eagle,
That's the way the money goes,
  Pop goes the weasel.

PORINGER

What is the rhyme for poringer?
The King he had a daughter fair,
And gave the Prince of Orange her!

ROBINSON CRUSOE

Poor old Robinson Crusoe!
Poor old Robinson Crusoe!
They made him a coat
Of an old Nanny goat,
I wonder how they could do so!
With a ring a ting tang
And a ring a ting tang.
Poor old Robinson Crusoe!

SCARING CROWS

O, all you little blacky tops,
Pray, don't you eat my father's crops,
While I lie down to take a nap.
   Shua-O! Shua-O!

If father he perchance should come,
With his cocked hat and his long gun,
Then you must fly and I must run.
   Shua-O! Shua-O!

SEE THE ROBBERS PASSING BY

See the robbers passing by,
   Passing by, passing by;
See the robbers passing by,
   My fair lady.

'What have the robbers done to you,
   Done to you, done to you;
What have the robbers done to you,
   My fair lady?'

'Broke the lock and stole the key,
   Stole the key, stole the key;
Broke the lock and stole the key!'
   My fair lady.

'How many pounds will set you free,
   Set you free, set you free;
How many pounds will set you free,
   My fair lady?'

'Twenty pounds will set you free,
   Set you free, set you free;
Twenty pounds will set you free,
   My fair lady.'

'So much money I have not got,
   Have not got, have not got;
So much money I have not got!'
   My fair lady.

'Then off to prison you must go,
   You must go, you must go;
Then off to prison you must go,
   My fair lady!'

SMITH, SMITH

'Smith, smith, beat them fine,
Can you shoe this horse of mine?'
'Yes, good sir, that I can,
As well as any other man:
Here a nail, and there a prod,
And now, good sir, your horse is shod.'

SNAIL, SNAIL

Snail, snail, shoot out your horns;
    Father and Mother are dead:
Brother and Sister are in the backyard,
    Begging for barley-bread.

SNEEZING

Sneeze on Monday, sneeze for danger;
Sneeze on Tuesday, miss a stranger;
Sneeze on Wednesday, get a letter;
Sneeze on Thursday, something better;
Sneeze on Friday, sneeze for sorrow,
Sneeze on Saturday, see your sweetheart to-morrow.

SOLOMON GRUNDY

Solomon Grundy,
Born on Monday,
Christened on Tuesday,
Married on Wednesday,
Took ill on Thursday,
Worse on Friday,
Died on Saturday,
Buried on Sunday,
So that was the end of Solomon Grundy.

A STAR

I have a little sister,
    Her name is Pretty Peep,
She wades in the waters
    Deep, deep, deep!

She climbs up the mountains
    High, high, high;
My poor little sister,
    She has but one eye.

THIS OLD MAN

This old man
He played One,
He played nick-nack on my drum.
    Nick-nack, paddy whack,
    Give a dog a bone,
    This old man came rolling home.

This old man
He played Two,
He played nick-nack on my shoe.
  Nick-nack, paddy whack . . .

This old man
He played Three,
He played nick-nack
On my knee.
  Nick-nack, paddy whack . . .

This old man
He played Four,
He played nick-nack
On my door.
  Nick-nack, paddy whack . . .

This old man,
He played Five,
He played nick-nack
On my hive.
  Nick-nack, paddy whack . . .

This old man
He played Six,
He played nick-nack
On my sticks.
  Nick-nack, paddy whack . . .

THREE LITTLE MICE

Three little mice sat down to spin.
Pussy passed by and she peeped in.
'What are you at, my fine little men?'
'Making coats for gentlemen.'
'Shall I come in and cut off your threads?'
'Oh no, Mistress Pussy, you'd bite off our heads!'

TOM, TOM,
THE PIPER'S SON

I

Tom, Tom, the piper's son,
He learned to play when he was young,
But all the tunes that he could play
Was 'Over the hills and far away.'
Over the hills and a great way off,
And the wind will blow my top-knot off.

II

Tom, Tom, the piper's son,
Stole a pig and away he run.
The pig was eat and Tom was beat,
And Tom went roaring down the street.

THE TUB

An old woman, I rub
    At the tub, tub, tub,
The clothes and the suds to rub, rub, rub;
    But when they are clean,
    And white to be seen,
I'll dress like a lady and dance on the green.

TO BED, TO BED

'To bed, to bed,' cried Sleepy-head.
'Tarry awhile,' said Slow.
Said Greedy Nan, 'Put on the pan,
Let's dine before we go.'

'To bed, to bed,' cried Sleepy-head.
But all the rest said, 'No!
It is morning now; you must milk the cow,
And to-morrow to bed we go.'

WE'RE ALL JOLLY BOYS

We're all jolly boys,
And we're coming with a noise.
Our coats shall be made
With fine lace brocade,
Our stockings shall be silk
As white as the milk,
And our tails shall touch
   the ground.

WHAT WILL YOU GIVE ME?

What will you give me for my pound?
Full twenty shillings round.
What will you give me for my shilling?
Twelve pence to give I'm willing.
What will you give me for my penny?
Four farthings, just so many.

CHRISTINA ROSSETTI

WEE WILLIE WINKIE

Wee Willie Winkie runs through the town,
Upstairs and downstairs in his night-gown.
Peeping through the window, crying through
   the lock,
'Are all the children in their beds? It's past
   eight o'clock.'

WHEN I WAS A LITTLE CHAP

When I was a little chap, I lived by myself,
And all the bread and cheese I got I put upon
    a shelf;
The rats and the mice did lead me such a life,
That I went to London to get myself a wife;
The streets were so broad, and the lanes were
    so narrow,
I could not get my wife home without a wheel-
    barrow.

WHITE SHEEP

White sheep, white sheep
    On a blue hill.
When the wind stops
    You all stand still.
You all run away
    When the winds blow;
White sheep, white sheep,
    Where do you go?

WYNKEN, BLYNKEN, AND NOD

Wynken, Blynken, and Nod one night
    Sailed off in a wooden shoe –
Sailed on a river of crystal light,
    Into a sea of dew.
'Where are you going, and what do you wish?'
    The old moon asked the three.
'We have come to fish for the herring fish

That live in this beautiful sea;
Nets of silver and gold have we!'
                    Said Wynken,
                    Blynken,
                    And Nod.

The old moon laughed and sang a song,
    As they rocked in the wooden shoe,
And the wind that sped them all night long
    Ruffled the waves of dew.
The little stars were the herring fish
    That lived in that beautiful sea –
'Now cast your nets wherever you wish –
    Never afeared are we;'
So cried the stars to the fishermen three;
                    Wynken,
                    Blynken,
                    And Nod.

All night long their nets they threw
    To the stars in the twinkling foam –
Then down from the skies came the wooden
        shoe,
    Bringing the fishermen home;
'Twas all so pretty a sail, it seemed
    As if it could not be,
And some folks thought 'twas a dream they'd
        dreamed
    Of sailing that beautiful sea –
But I shall name you the fishermen three:
                    Wynken,
                    Blynken,
                    And Nod.

Wynken and Blynken are two little eyes,
   And Nod is a little head,
And the wooden shoe that sailed the skies
   Is a wee one's trundle bed.
So shut your eyes while mother sings,
   Of wonderful sights that be,
And you shall see the beautiful things
   As you rock in the misty sea,
Where the old shoe rocked the fishermen
      three:
               Wynken,
               Blynken,
               And Nod.   EUGENE FIELD

YANKEE DOODLE

Yankee Doodle came to town
   Upon a little pony;
He stuck a feather in his cap
   And called it macaroni.

Yankee doodle, doodle do,
   Yankee doodle dandy;
All the lasses are so smart,
   And sweet as sugar candy.

First he bought a porridge pot,
   Then he bought a ladle,
Then he trotted home again
   As fast as he was able.

Yankee doodle, doodle. . . .

Marching in and marching out,
    And marching round the town O!
Here there comes a regiment
    With Captain Thomas Brown O!

Yankee doodle, doodle....

Yankee Doodle is a tune
    That comes in mighty handy;
The enemy all runs away
    At Yankee doodle dandy.

Yankee doodle, doodle....

YELLOW WHEELS

A yellow gig has Farmer Patch;
    He drives a handsome mare –
Two bright wheels and four bright hooves
    To carry him to the fair.

Yellow wheels, where are you off to,
    Twinkling down the lane,
Sparkling in the April sunshine
    And the April rain?

Farmer Patch we do not love;
    He wears a crusty frown.
But how we love to see his gig
    Go spanking off to town!

Yellow wheels, where are you off to,
    Twinkling down the lane,
Sparkling in the April sunshine
    And the April rain?

JAMES REEVES

PART TWO
GREY GOOSE AND GANDER

A DIS, A DIS

A dis, a dis, a green grass,
  A dis, a dis, a dis;
Come, all you pretty fair maids
  And dance along with us.

For we are going roving,
  A-roving in this land;
We take this pretty fair maid,
  We take her by the hand.

She shall get a duke, my dear,
  As duck do get a drake;
And she shall have a young prince
  For her own fair sake.

And if this young prince chance to die,
  She shall get another;
The bells will ring, and the birds will sing,
  And we clap hands together.

AS I WAS GOING TO BANBURY

As I was going to Banbury,
  Ri-fol lat-i-tee O,
As I was going to Banbury
I saw a fine codlin apple tree,
  With a ri-fol lat-i-tee O.

And when the codlins began to fall,
  Ri-fol . . .
I found five hundred men in all,
  With a ri-fol . . .

And one of the men I saw was dead,
  Ri-fol . . .
So I sent for a hatchet to open his head,
  With a ri-fol . . .

And in his head I found a spring,
  Ri-fol . . .
And seven young salmon a-learning to sing,
  With a ri-fol . . .

And one of the salmon as big as I,
  Ri-fol . . .
Now do you not think I am telling a lie?
  With a ri-fol . . .

And one of the salmon as big as an elf,
  Ri-fol . . .
If you want any more, you must sing
    it yourself!
  With a ri-fol . . .

THE BABES IN THE WOOD

My dear, do you know
How a long time ago
   Two poor little children
Whose names I don't know
Were stolen away
On a fine summer's day
   And left in a wood,
As I've heard people say.

And when it was night,
So sad was their plight,
   The sun it went down
And the moon gave no light!
They sobbed and they sighed,
And they bitterly cried,
   And the poor little things,
They laid down and died.

The robins so red
Brought strawberry leaves
   And over them spread,
And all the day long
They sang them this song:
Poor babes in the wood!
Poor babes in the wood!
   And don't you remember
The babes in the wood?

BUY ME A MILKING-PAIL

'Buy me a milking-pail,
  Mother, mother.'
'Betsy's gone a-milking,
  Beautiful daughter.'

'Sell my father's feather-bed,
  Mother, mother.'
'Where will your father lie,
  Beautiful daughter?'

'Put him in the boys' bed,
  Mother, mother.'
'Where will the boys lie,
  Beautiful daughter?'

'Put them in the pig-sty,
  Mother, mother.'
'Where will the pigs lie,
  Beautiful daughter?'

'Put them in the salting tub,
  Mother, mother.
Put them in the salting tub,
  Mother, mother.'

A COUGH

I have a little cough, sir,
In my little chest, sir,
Every time I cough, sir,
It leaves a little pain, sir,
Cough,* cough, cough, cough,
There it is again, sir.

ROBERT GRAVES

* *Or* Ahem, ahem, ahem, ahem.

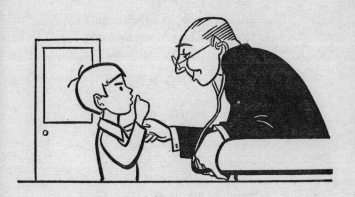

DAME, GET UP AND BAKE
YOUR PIES

Dame, get up and bake your pies,
  Bake your pies, bake your pies;
Dame, get up and bake your pies,
  On Christmas Day in the morning.

Dame, what makes your maidens lie,
    Maidens lie, maidens lie;
Dame, what makes your maidens lie,
    On Christmas Day in the morning?

Dame, what makes your ducks to die,
    Ducks to die, ducks to die;
Dame, what makes your ducks to die,
    On Christmas Day in the morning?

Their wings are cut, and they cannot fly,
    Cannot fly, cannot fly;
Their wings are cut, and they cannot fly,
    On Christmas Day in the morning.

DASHING AWAY

'Twas on a Monday morning
When I beheld my darling;
She looked so neat and charming
In every high degree;
She looked so neat and nimble, O,
Washing of her linen, O! –
Dashing away with a smoothing iron,
Dashing away with a smoothing iron,
She stole my heart away.

'Twas on a Tuesday morning,
When I beheld my darling;
She looked so neat and charming
In every high degree;

She looked so neat and nimble, O,
Hanging out her linen, O! –
Dashing away . . .

'Twas on a Wednesday morning,
When I beheld . . .
She looked so neat and nimble, O,
Starching of her linen, O! –
Dashing away . . .

'Twas on a Thursday morning
When I beheld . . .
She looked so neat and nimble, O,
Ironing of her linen, O! –
Dashing away . . .

'Twas on a Friday morning,
When I beheld . . .
She looked so neat and nimble, O,
Folding of her linen, O! –
Dashing away . . .

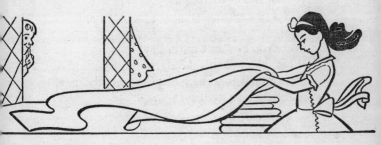

'Twas on a Saturday morning,
When I beheld . . .
She looked so neat and nimble, O,
Airing of her linen, O! –
Dashing away . . .

'Twas on a Sunday morning,
When I beheld . . .
She looked so neat and nimble, O,
Wearing of her linen, O! –
Dashing away . . .

DONKEY RIDING

Were you ever in Quebec,
Stowing timbers on a deck,
Where there's a king in his golden crown
   Riding on a donkey?

Hey ho, and away we go,
   Donkey riding, donkey riding,
Hey ho, and away we go,
   Riding on a donkey.

Were you ever in Cardiff Bay,
Where the folks all shout, Hooray!
Here comes John with his three months' pay,
   Riding on a donkey?

Hey ho, and away . . .

Were you ever off Cape Horn,
Where it's always fine and warm?
See the lion and the unicorn
  Riding on a donkey.

  Hey ho, and away . . .

ELSIE MARLEY

Do you ken Elsie Marley, honey?
The wife who sells the barley, honey?
She won't get up to feed the swine,
And do you ken Elsie Marley, honey?

Elsie Marley's grown so fine
She won't get up to feed the swine
But lies in bed till eight or nine,
And surely she does take her time.

ELVES' DANCE

By the moon we sport and play,
With the night begins our day:
As we frisk the dew doth fall.
Trip it, little urchins* all!
Lightly as the little bee,
Two by two, and three by three.
And about go we, and about go we!

JOHN LYLY

* Elves.

73

THE FAIRIES OF THE
CALDON LOW

'And where have you been, my Mary,
   And where have you been from me?'
'I've been to the top of the Caldon Low,
   The midsummer night to see!'

'And what did you see, my Mary,
   All up on the Caldon Low?'
'I saw the glad sunshine come down,
   And I saw the merry winds blow.'

'And what did you hear, my Mary,
   All up on the Caldon Hill?'
'I heard the drops of the waters made,
   And the ears of the green corn fill.'

'Oh! tell me all, my Mary,
   All, all that ever you know;
For you must have seen the fairies
   Last night on the Caldon Low.'

'Then take me on your knee, mother;
    And listen, mother of mine.
A hundred fairies danced last night,
    And the harpers they were nine.

'And their harp-strings rang so merrily
    To their dancing feet so small;
But oh! the words of their talking
    Were merrier far than all.'

'And what were the words, my Mary,
    That then you heard them say?'
'I'll tell you all, my mother;
    But let me have my way.

'Some of them played with the water,
    And rolled it down the hill.
"And this," they said, "shall speedily turn
    The poor old miller's mill:

'"For there has been no water
    Ever since the first of May;
And a busy man will the miller be
    At the dawning of the day.

'"Oh! the miller, how he will laugh
    When he sees the mill dam rise!
The jolly old miller, how he will laugh,
    Till the tears fill both his eyes!"

'And some they seized the little winds
    That sounded over the hill;
And each put a horn into his mouth,
    And blew both loud and shrill.

'"And there," they said, "the merry winds
    go
    Away from every horn;
And they shall clear the mildew dank
    From the blind old widow's corn.

'"Oh! the poor blind widow,
    Though she has been blind so long,
She'll be blithe enough when the mildew's
    gone,
    And the corn stands tall and strong."

'And some they brought the brown lint-
    seed,
    And flung it down from the Low;
"And this," they said, "by the sunrise
    In the weaver's croft shall grow.

'"Oh! the poor lame weaver,
    How he will laugh outright,
When he sees his dwindling flax-field
    All full of flowers by night!"

'And then out spoke a brownie,
   With a long beard on his chin;
"I have spun up all the tow," said he,
   "And I want some more to spin.

'"I've spun a piece of hempen cloth,
   And I want to spin another;
A little sheet for Mary's bed,
   And an apron for her mother."

'With that I could not help but laugh,
   And I laughed out loud and free;
And then on the top of the Caldon Low
   There was no one left but me.

'And all on the top of the Caldon Low
   The mists were cold and grey,
And nothing I saw but the mossy stones
   That round about me lay.

'But coming down from the hill-top,
   I heard afar below
How busy the jolly miller was
   And how the wheel did go.

'And I peeped into the widow's field,
    And, sure enough, were seen
The yellow ears of the mildewed corn,
    All standing stout and green.

'And down to the weaver's croft I stole,
    To see if the flax were sprung;
But I met the weaver at his gate,
    With the good news on his tongue.

'Now this is all I heard, mother,
    And all that I did see;
So, prithee make my bed, mother,
    For I'm tired as I can be.'

MARY HOWITT

THE FAIRY QUEEN

Come follow, follow me,
You, fairy elves that be:
Which circle on the green,
Come follow Mab, your queen.
Hand in hand let's dance around,
For this place is fairy ground,

When mortals are at rest,
And snoring in their nest;
Unheard and unespied,
Through keyholes we do glide;
Over tables, stools and shelves,
We trip it with our fairy elves.

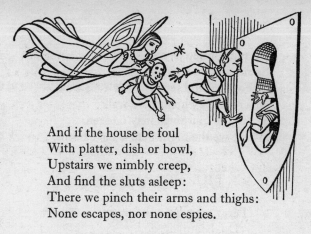

And if the house be foul
With platter, dish or bowl,
Upstairs we nimbly creep,
And find the sluts asleep:
There we pinch their arms and thighs:
None escapes, nor none espies.

But if the house be swept,
And from uncleanness kept,
We praise the household maid,
And duly she is paid:
For we use before we go
To drop a tester* in her shoe.

Upon a mushroom's head
Our table-cloth we spread;
A grain of rye or wheat,
Is manchet† which we eat;
Pearly drops of dew we drink
In acorn cups filled to the brink.

The grasshopper, gnat and fly
Serve for our minstrelsy;
Grace said, we dance awhile,
And so the time is beguile,
And if the moon doth hide her head,
The glow-worm lights us home to bed.

* Sixpence.   † Food.

On tops of dewy grass
So nimbly do we pass,
The young and tender stalk
Ne'er bends when we do walk;
Yet in the mornings may be seen
Where we the night before have been.

THE FERRYMAN

'Ferry me across the water,
    Do, boatman, do.'
'If you've a penny in your purse,
    I'll ferry you.'

'I have a penny in my purse,
    And my eyes are blue;
So ferry me across the water,
    Do boatman, do.'

'Step into my ferry-boat,
    Be they black or blue,
And for the penny in your purse
    I'll ferry you.'

CHRISTINA ROSSETTI

THE FOX

The fox went out one winter night,
And prayed the moon to give him light,
For he'd many a mile to go that night,
    Before he reached his den, oh!

Chorus. Den, oh! Den, oh!
  For he'd many a mile to go that night,
  He'd many a mile to go that night,
    Before he reached his den, oh!

At last he came to a farmer's yard,
Where the ducks and geese were all afear'd
'The best of you all shall grease my beard,
  Before I leave the town, oh!'
Chorus. Town, oh! Town, oh!
  'The best of you all . . .'

He took the grey goose by the neck,
He laid a duck across his back,
And heeded not their quack! quack! quack!
  The legs all dangling down, oh!
Chorus. Down, oh! Down oh!
  And heeded not their . . .

Then old Mother Slipper Slopper jumped out of bed
And out of the window she popped her head,
Crying, 'Oh! John, John! the grey goose is dead,
  And the fox is over the down, oh!'
Chorus. Down, oh! Down, oh!
  Crying, 'Oh! John, John! . . .'

Then John got up to the top of the hill,
And blew his horn both loud and shrill,
'Blow on,' said Reynard, 'your music still,
  Whilst I trot home to my den, oh!'
Chorus. Den, oh, Den, oh!
  'Blow on,' said Reynard . . .

At last he came to his cosy den,
Where sat his young ones nine or ten.
Quoth they, 'Daddy, you must go there again,
    For sure 'tis a lucky town, oh!'
Chorus. Town, oh! Town, oh!
    Quoth they, 'Daddy . . .'

The fox and wife without any strife,
They cut up the goose without fork or knife,
And said 'twas the best they had ate in their life,
    And the young ones picked the bones, Oh!
Chorus. Bones, oh! Bones, oh!
    And said 'twas the best . . .

A FOX JUMPED UP

A fox jumped up on a moonlight night,
The stars were shining and all things bright:
'Oh, oh!' said the fox, 'it's a very fine night
For me to go through the town, heigho!'

The fox when he came to yonder stile,
He lifted his ears, and he listened awhile;
'Oh, oh!' said the fox, ''tis but a short mile
From this to yonder town, heigho!'

The fox, when he came to the farmer's gate,
Whom should he see but the farmer's drake?
'I love you too well for your master's sake,
And I long to be picking your bones, heigho!'

The grey goose she ran around the haystack,
'Oh, oh!' said the fox, 'you are very fat,
And you'll do very well to ride on my back
From this to yonder town, heigho!'

The farmer's wife she jumped out of bed,
And out of the window she popped her head,
And she cried 'Oh, husband! the geese are all dead,
For the fox has been through the town, heigho!'

The farmer loaded his pistol with lead,
And shot the old rogue of a fox through the head.
'Ah, ah!' said the farmer, 'I think you are dead,
And no more will you trouble the town, heigho!'

GREY

Grey is the sky, and grey the woodman's cot
With grey smoke tumbling from the chimney-pot.
The flagstones are grey that lead to the door;
Grey is the hearth, and grey the worn old floor.

The old man by the fire nods in his chair;
Grey are his clothes and silvery grey his hair.
Grey are the shadows around him creeping,
And grey the mouse from the corner peeping.

JAMES REEVES

GREY GOOSE AND GANDER

Grey goose and gander,
Waft your wings together,
And carry the good king's daughter
Over the one-strand river.

HIST WHIST

hist   whist
little ghostthings
tip-toe
twinkle-toe

little twitchy
witches and tingling
goblins
hob-a-nob   hob-a-nob

little hoppy happy
toad in tweeds
tweeds
little itchy mousies

with scuttling
eyes   rustle and run   and
hidehidehide
whist

whisk   look out for the old woman
with the wart on her nose
what she'll do to yer
nobody knows

for she knows the devil   ooch
the devil   ouch
the devil
ach   the great

green
dancing
devil
devil

devil
devil
　　　　wheeEEE

E. E. CUMMINGS

I SAW THREE SHIPS

I saw three ships come sailing by,
On Christmas Day, on Christmas Day,
I saw three ships come sailing by,
　On Christmas Day in the morning.

And who was in those ships all three,
   On Christmas Day, on Christmas Day,
And who was in those ships all three,
   On Christmas Day in the morning?

Our Saviour Christ and his lady,
   On Christmas Day, on Christmas Day,
Our Saviour Christ and his lady,
   On Christmas Day in the morning.

Oh! they sailed into Bethlehem,
   On Christmas Day, on Christmas Day,
Oh! they sailed into Bethlehem,
   On Christmas Day in the morning.

And all the bells on earth shall ring,
   On Christmas Day, on Christmas Day,
And all the bells on earth shall ring,
   On Christmas Day in the morning.

And all the Angels in Heaven shall sing,
   On Christmas Day, on Christmas Day,
And all the Angels in Heaven shall sing,
   On Christmas Day in the morning.

And all the souls on earth shall sing,
   On Christmas Day, on Christmas Day,
And all the souls on earth shall sing,
   On Christmas Day in the morning.

IF ALL THE WORLD
WERE PAPER

If all the world were paper,
  If all the sea were ink,
If all the trees were bread and cheese,
  What would we have to drink?

  If all the bottles leaked
    And none but had a crack,
If Spanish apes ate all the grapes,
  What would we do for sack?*

* Wine.

JENNY WREN

Jenny Wren fell sick;
  Upon a merry time,
In came Robin Redbreast,
  And brought her sops of wine.

  'Eat well of the sop, Jenny,
    Drink well of the wine.'
  'Thank you, Robin, kindly,
    You shall be mine.'

  Jenny she got well,
    And stood upon her feet,
  And told Robin plainly
    She loved him not a bit.

Robin, being angry,
   Hopp'd on a twig:
'Out upon you, fie upon you,
   Bold-faced jig!'

THE KEEPER

The keeper did a-shooting go,
And under his cloak he carried a bow
All for to shoot at a merry little doe,
   Among the leaves so green, O!

CHORUS
1st voice. Jackie boy!
2nd voice.   Master!
1.   Sing ye well?
2.   Very well.
1.   Hey down!
2.   Ho down!
1 and 2.   Derry derry down,
            Among the leaves so green, O!
1.   To my hey down down!
2.   To my ho down down!
1.   Hey down!
2.   Ho down!
1 and 2.   Derry derry down,
            Among the leaves so green, O!

The first doe he shot at he missed,
The second doe he trimmed, he kissed,

The third doe went where nobody wist,*
  Among the leaves so green, O!

Chorus.

The fourth doe she did cross the plain;
The keeper fetched her back again;
Where she is now she may remain,
  Among the leaves so green, O!

Chorus.

The fifth doe she did cross the brook;
The keeper fetched her back with his crook;
Where she is now you must go and look,
  Among the leaves so green, O!

Chorus.

The sixth doe she ran over the plain;
But he with his hounds did turn her again,
And it's there he did hunt in a merry, merry
    vein,
  Among the leaves so green, O!

Chorus.

* Knew.

KING STEPHEN

King Stephen had a story teller and gave him
    princely pay
To tell him stories after supper, a new one
    every day:
But when the stories failed him (this Andrew
    did agree)
The King would call his merry men all and
    hang him from a tree.

Andrew had told five hundred tales and found
    no more to tell:
He started from the first once more, and
    Stephen knew it well.
'Old friends are best,' the monarch cried, 'and
    old yarns spun again.
Tell me the story of Jack o'Binnorie every night
    of my reign.'

ROBERT GRAVES

THE LADY AND THE SWINE

There was a lady loved a swine.
    'Honey,' said she,
'Pig-hog, wilt thou be mine?'
    'Hunc,' said he.

'I'll build for thee a silver sty,
    Honey,' said she,
'And in it softly thou shalt lie.'
    'Hunc,' said he.

'Pinned with a silver pin,
    Honey,' said she,
'That you may go both out and in.'
    'Hunc,' said he.

'When shall we two be wed,
    Honey?' said she.
'Hunc, hunc, hunc,' he said,
    And away went he.

LITTLE CLOTILDA

Little Clotilda,
    Well and hearty,
Thought she'd like
    To give a party.
But as her friends
    Were shy and wary,
Nobody came
    But her own canary.

THE MAN IN THE WILDERNESS

The man in the wilderness asked of me
'How many strawberries grow in the sea?'
I answered him as I thought good,
'As many red herrings as grow in the wood.'

'Now pray, where are you going, child?' said
Meet-on-the-Road.

'To school, sir, to school, sir,' said Child-as-it-
Stood.

'What have you got in your basket, child?' said
Meet-on-the-Road.

'My dinner, sir, my dinner, sir,' said Child-as-
it-Stood.

'What have you for your dinner, child?' said
Meet-on-the-Road.

'Some pudding, sir, some pudding, sir,' said
Child-as-it-Stood.

'Oh then, I pray, give me a share,' said Meet-on-
the-Road.

'I've little enough for myself, sir,' said Child-as-
it-Stood.

'What have you got that cloak on for?' said Meet-
on-the-Road.

'To keep the wind and the cold from me,' said
Child-as-it-Stood.

'I wish the wind would blow through you,' said
    Meet-on-the-Road.
'Oh, what a wish! Oh, what a wish!' said Child-
    as-it-Stood.
'Pray, what are those bells ringing for?' said
    Meet-on-the-Road.
'To ring bad spirits home again,' said Child-as-
    it-Stood.
'Oh, then I must be going, child!' said Meet-on-
    the-Road.
'So fare you well, so fare you well,' said Child-as-
    it-Stood.

MAY SONG

Trip and go! heave and ho!
Up and down, to and fro,
From the town to the grove
Two and two let us rove
A-maying, a-playing:
Love hath no gainsaying,
So merrily trip and go!

THOMAS NASHE

MIRROR, MIRROR

Mirror, mirror, tell me,
    Am I pretty or plain?
Or am I downright ugly
    And ugly to remain?

Shall I marry a gentleman?
　　Shall I marry a clown?
Or shall I marry old Knives-and-Scissors
　　Shouting through the town?

MR NOBODY

I know a funny little man,
　　As quiet as a mouse,
Who does the mischief that is done
　　In everybody's house!
There's no one ever sees his face,
　　And yet we all agree
That every plate we break was cracked
　　By Mr Nobody.

'Tis he who always tears our books,
　　Who leaves the door ajar,
He pulls the buttons from our shirts,
　　And scatters pins afar;
That squeaking door will always squeak,
　　For prithee, don't you see,
We leave the oiling to be done
　　By Mr Nobody.

He puts damp wood upon the fire,
　　That kettles cannot boil;
His are the feet that bring in mud,
　　And all the carpets soil.
The papers always are mislaid,
　　Who had them last but he?
There's no one tosses them about
　　But Mr Nobody.

The finger-marks upon the door
   By none of us are made;
We never leave the blinds unclosed,
   To let the curtains fade.
The ink we never spill; the boots
   That lying round you see
Are not our boots; – they all belong
   To Mr Nobody.

MY UNCLE JEHOSHAPHAT

My Uncle Jehoshaphat had a pig,
   A pig of high degree;
And it always wore a brown scratch wig,
   Most beautiful for to see.

My Uncle Jehoshaphat loved that pig,
   And the piggy-wig he loved him;
And they both jumped into the lake one day,
   To see which best could swim.

My Uncle Jehoshaphat he swam up,
   And the piggy-wig he swam down;
And so they both did win the prize,
   Which the same was a velvet gown.

A NAIL

For want of a nail, the shoe was lost;
For want of a shoe, the horse was lost;
For want of a horse, the rider was lost;
For want of a rider, the battle was lost;
For want of a battle, the kingdom was lost
And all for want of a horseshoe nail.

O COME, LET US SING

O come, let us sing unto the Lord; let us make
a joyful noise to the rock of our salvation.

Let us come before his presence with thanks-
giving, and make a joyful noise unto him with
psalms.

For the Lord is a great God, and a great King
above all Gods.

In his hand are the deep places of the earth: the strength of the hills is his also.

The sea is his, and he made it: and his hands formed the dry land.

from PSALM 95

O MY PRETTY COCK

O my pretty cock, my pretty crowing cock,
   I pray you do not crow before day,
And your comb shall be made of the very
     beaten gold,
   And your wings of the silver so grey!

THE OLD MAN IN
THE WOOD

There was an old man who lived in a wood,
   As you may plainly see;
He said he could do as much work in a day
   As his wife could do in three.
'With all my heart,' the old woman said,
   'If that you will allow
Tomorrow you'll stay at home in my stead,
   And I'll go drive the plough.

'But you must milk the tidy cow
   For fear that she go dry,
And you must feed the little pigs
   That are within the sty:

And you must mind the speckled hen
   For fear she lay astray,
And you must reel the spool of yarn
   That I spun yesterday.'

The old woman took a staff in her hand,
   And went to drive the plough:
The old man took a pail in his hand
   And went to milk the cow.
But Tidy hinched and Tidy flinched,
   And Tidy broke his nose,
And Tidy gave him such a blow
   That the blood ran down to his toes.

'High! Tidy! Ho! Tidy! High!
   Tidy! do stand still.
If ever I milk you, Tidy, again,
   'Twill be sore against my will.'
He went to feed the little pigs
   That were within the sty,
He hit his head against the beam,
   And he made the blood to fly.

He went to mind the speckled hen
   For fear she'd laid astray,
And he forgot the spool of yarn
   His wife spun yesterday.
So he swore by the sun, the moon and the
     stars,
   And the green leaves on the tree,
If his wife didn't do a day's work in her life,
   She should never be ruled by he.

THE OLD MAN ON
THE BORDER

There was an Old Man on the Border,
Who lived in the utmost disorder;
   He danced with the Cat,
   And made Tea in his Hat,
Which vexed all the folks on the Border.

EDWARD LEAR

OLIVER CROMWELL

Oliver Cromwell's buried and dead,
   He, hi, buried and dead.
There grew a ripe apple-tree over his head,
   He, hi, over his head.
The apples were ripe and ready to fall,
   He, hi, ready to fall.
There came an old woman and gathered them all,
   He, hi, gathered them all.
Oliver rose and gave her a clop,
   He, hi, gave her a clop,
Which made the old woman go hippertihop,
   He, hi, hippertihop.
Saddle and bridle are laid on the shelf,
   He, hi, laid on the shelf;
If you want any more you can sing it yourself,
   He, hi, sing it yourself.

ONE MAN SHALL MOW
MY MEADOW

One man shall mow my meadow,
Two men shall gather it together,
Two men, one man, and one more
Shall shear my lambs and ewes and rams,
And gather my gold together.
Three men shall mow my meadow,
Four men shall gather it together,
Four men, three men, two men, one man, and
   one more
Shall shear my lambs and ewes and rams,
And gather my gold together.

Five men shall mow my meadow,
Six men shall gather it together,
Six men, five men, four men . . .

(*and so on, as long as you like*)

THE PENNY FIDDLE

Yesterday I bought a penny fiddle
And put it to my chin to play,
But I found that the strings were painted
So I threw my fiddle away.

A little red man found my fiddle
As it lay abandoned there;
He asked me if he might keep it,
And I told him I did not care.

But he drew such music from the fiddle
    With help of a farthing bow
That I offered five guineas for the secret
    But, alas, he would never let it go.

ROBERT GRAVES

A PRAYER

Matthew, Mark, Luke and John,
Bless the bed that I lie on:
Four corners to my bed,
Four angels round my head,
One to watch, one to pray,
Two to bear my soul away.

THE PUMPKIN

You may not believe it, for hardly could I:
I was cutting a pumpkin to put in a pie,
And on it was written in letters most plain
'You may hack me in slices, but I'll grow again.'

I seized it and sliced it and made no mistake
As, with dough rounded over, I put it to bake:
But soon in the garden as I chanced to walk,
Why, there was that pumpkin entire on his stalk!

ROBERT GRAVES

RIDDLES

(Answers on page 117)

I

Little Nancy Etticoat,
In a white petticoat,
And a red nose;
The longer she stands,
The shorter she grows.

2

In marble halls as white as milk,
Lined with a skin as soft as silk,
Within a fountain crystal-clear
A golden apple doth appear.
No doors are there to this stronghold,
Yet thieves break in and steal the gold.

3

HEAD AND EYE

There is one that has a head without an eye,
   And there's one that has an eye without a head:
You may find the answer if you try;
   And when all is said,
Half the answer hangs upon a thread.

CHRISTINA ROSSETTI

4

The winds they did blow,
   The leaves they did wag;
Along came a beggar boy
   And put me in his bag.

He took me up to London,
   A lady did me buy,
Put me in a silver cage,
   And hung me up on high.

With apples by the fire
   And nuts for to crack,
Besides a little feather bed
   To ease my little back.

5

I went to the wood and got it,
I sat me down and looked for it.
The more I searched for it the less I liked it,
And I brought it home because I couldn't find it.

There was a little green house,
And in the little green house
There was a little brown house,
And in the little brown house
There was a little yellow house,
And in the little yellow house
There was a little white house,
And in the little white house
There was a little heart.

RILLOBY-RILL

Grasshoppers four a-fiddling went,
   Heigh-ho! never be still!
They earned but little towards their rent
But all day long with their elbows bent
   They fiddled a tune called Rilloby-rilloby,
   Fiddled a tune called Rilloby-rill.

Grasshoppers soon on fairies came,
   Heigh-ho! never be still!
Fairies asked with a manner of blame,
'Where do you come from, what is your name,
   What do you want with your Rilloby-rilloby,
   What do you want with your Rilloby-rill?'

'Madam, you see before you stand,
   Heigh-ho! never be still!
The Old Original Favourite Grand
Grasshoppers' Green Herbarian Band,
   And the tune we play is Rilloby-rilloby,
   Madam, the tune is Rilloby-rill.'

Fairies hadn't a word to say,
   Heigh-ho! never be still!
Fairies seldom are sweet by day,
But the grasshoppers merrily fiddled away,
   Oh, but they played with a willoby-rilloby,
   Oh, but they played with a willoby-will!

Fairies slumber and sulk at noon,
   Heigh-ho! never be still!
But at last the kind old motherly moon
Brought them dew in a silver spoon,
   And they turned to ask for Rilloby-rilloby,
   One more round of Rilloby-rill.

Ah, but nobody now replied,
   Heigh-ho! never be still!
When day went down the music died,
Grasshoppers four lay side by side.
   And there was an end of their Rilloby-rilloby,
   And there was an end of their Rilloby-rill.

HENRY NEWBOLT

THE SIX BADGERS

As I was a-hoeing, a-hoeing my lands
Six badgers came up with white wands in their hands.
They made a ring around me and, bowing, they said:
'Hurry home, Farmer George, for the table is spread!
There's pie in the oven, there's beef on the plate:
Hurry home, Farmer George, if you would not be late!'
So homeward I went, but could not understand
Why six fine dog-badgers with white wands in hand
Should seek me out hoeing and bow in a ring,
And all to inform me so common a thing!

ROBERT GRAVES

SPEAK ROUGHLY TO YOUR
LITTLE BOY

Speak roughly to your little boy,
    And beat him when he sneezes:
He only does it to annoy,
    Because he knows it teases.

WOW! WOW! WOW!

I speak severely to my boy,
   I beat him when he sneezes;
For he can thoroughly enjoy
   The pepper when he pleases.

WOW! WOW! WOW!

LEWIS CARROLL

SPREAD, TABLE, SPREAD

Spread, table, spread,
Meat, drink and bread,
Ever may I have
What I ever crave,
When I am spread,
Meat for my black cock,
And meat for my red.

GEORGE PEELE

THE TAILOR AND THE CROW

A carrion crow sat on an oak,
   Fol-de-riddle, lol-de-riddle, hi ding do,
Watching a tailor shape his cloak;
   Sing hey ho, the carrion crow,
   Fol-de-riddle, lol-de-riddle, hi ding do.

'Wife, bring me my old bent bow,
   Fol-de-riddle, lol-de-riddle, hi ding do,
That I may shoot yon carrion crow',

Sing hey ho, the carrion crow,
Fol-de-riddle, lol-de-riddle, hi ding do.

The tailor he shot and missed his mark,
  Fol-de-riddle, lol-de-riddle, hi ding do,
And shot his own sow quite through the heart;
  Sing, hey go, the carrion crow,
  Fol-de-riddle, lol-de-riddle, hi ding do!

'Wife, bring brandy in a spoon,
  Fol-de-riddle, lol-de-riddle, hi ding do,
For our old sow is in a swoon';
  Sing hey ho, the carrion crow,
  Fol-de-riddle, lol-de-riddle, hi ding do.

THERE WAS A MONKEY

There was a monkey climbed up a tree,
When he fell down, then down fell he.

There was crow sat on a stone,
When he was gone, then there was none.

There was a horse going to the mill,
When he went on, he stood not still.

There was an old wife did eat an apple,
When she had ate two, she had ate a couple.

There was a butcher cut his thumb,
When it did bleed, then blood did come.

There was lackey ran a race,
When he ran fast, he ran apace.

There was a navy went into Spain,
When it returned, it came again.

THERE WAS AN OLD WOMAN

There was an old woman, as I've heard tell,
She went to market her eggs for to sell;
She went to market all on a market day,
And she fell asleep on the king's highway.

There came by a pedlar whose name was Stout,
He cut her petticoats all round about;
He cut her petticoats up to the knees,
Which made the old woman to shiver and freeze.

When this little woman first did wake,
She began to shiver and she began to shake,
She began to wonder and she began to cry,
'Lauk a mercy on me, this is none of I!

'But if it be I, as I do hope it be,
I've a little dog at home, and he'll know me;
If it be I, he'll wag his little tail,
And if it be not I, he'll loudly bark and wail.'

Home went the little woman all in the dark,
Up got the little dog, and he began to bark;
He began to bark, so she began to cry,
'Lauk a mercy on me, this is none of I!'

THERE WAS AN OLD WOMAN OF SURREY

There was an old woman of Surrey,
Who was morn, noon, and night in a hurry;
 Called her husband a fool,
 Drove her children to school,
The worrying old woman of Surrey.

TOM THUMB

Here lies Tom Thumb, King Arthur's knight,
Who died by a spider's cruel bite;
He was well known in Arthur's court,
Where he afforded gallant sport;
He rode at tilt and tournament,
And on a mouse a-hunting went.

Alive, he filled the court with mirth;
His death to sorrow soon gave birth.
Wipe, wipe your eyes, and shake your head
And cry 'Alas! Tom Thumb is dead!'

TWEEDLEDUM AND TWEEDLEDEE

Tweedledum and Tweedledee
   Went down to have a battle,
For Tweedledum said Tweedledee
   Had spoilt his penny rattle.
Just then flew by a monstrous crow,
   As big as a tar-barrel,
Which frightened both the heroes so,
   They quite forgot their quarrel.

TRIP UPON TRENCHERS

Trip upon trenchers, and dance upon dishes,
My mother sent me for balm, for balm:
She bade me tread lightly, and come again quickly,
For fear as I went I should come to some harm.

THE TWELVE OXEN

I have twelve oxen that be fair and brown,
And they go a-grazing down by the town. –
    With hey! with how! with hey!
Sawest not you mine oxen, you little pretty boy?

I have twelve oxen, they be fair and white,
And they go a-grazing down by the dyke. –
    With hey! with how! with hey!
Sawest not you mine oxen, you little pretty boy?

I have twelve oxen, and they be fair and black,
And they go a-grazing down by the lake. –
    With hey! with how! with hey!
Sawest not you mine oxen, you little pretty boy?

I have twelve oxen, and they be fair and red,
And they go a-grazing down by the mead. –
    With hey! with how! with hey!
Sawest not you mine oxen, you little pretty boy?

THE TWO RATS

He was a rat, and she was a rat,
    And down in one hole they did dwell,
And both were as black as a witch's cat,
    And they loved one another well.

He had a tail, and she had a tail,
    Both long and curling and fine;
And each said, 'Yours is the finest tail
    In the world excepting mine.'

He smelt the cheese, and she smelt the cheese,
    And they both pronounced it good;
And both remarked it would greatly add
    To the charms of their daily food.

So he ventured out, and she ventured out,
    And I saw them go with pain,
But what befell them I never can tell,
    For they never came back again.

THE WARS OF THE ROSES

Huff the Talbot* and our cat Tib
    They took up sword and shield,
'Tip for the red rose, Huff for the white,
    To fight upon Bosworth Field.

* A kind of dog.

114

Oh, it was dreary that night to bury
   Those doughty warriors dead;
Under a white rose brave dog Huff,
   And fierce Tib under a red.

Low lay Huff and long may he lie!
   But our Tib took little harm:
He was up and away at dawn of day
   With the rose-bush under his arm.

WHAT'S IN THERE?

What's in there?
Gold and money.
Where's my share of it?
The moosie ran awa' wi't.
Where's the moosie?
In her hoosie.
Where's her hoosie?
In the wood.
Where's the wood?
The fire burnt it.
Where's the fire?
The water quenched it.
Where's the water?
The broon bull drank it.
Where's the broon bull?
Back o' Burnie's hill.
Where's Burnie's hill?
A'clad wi' snaw.
Where's the snaw?
The sun melted it.
Where's the sun?
High, high, up i' the air!

WISHES

If wishes were horses,
    Beggars would ride;
If turnips were watches,
    I would wear one by my side.

1. A Candle. 2. An Egg. 3. Pin and Needle. 4. A Squirrel.

5. A Thorn. 6. A Walnut.

PART THREE

GREEN BROOM

ALL IN THE MORNING

It was on Christmas Day,
  And all in the morning,
Our Saviour was born
  And our heavenly king:
    And was not this a joyful thing!
    And sweet Jesus they called him by name.

It was on the Twelfth Day,
  And all in the morning,
The Wise Men were led
  To our heavenly king:
    And was not this a joyful thing?
    And sweet Jesus they called him by name.

It was on Holy Wednesday,
  And all in the morning,
That Judas betrayed

Our dear heavenly king:
　　And was not this a woeful thing?
　　And sweet Jesus we'll call him by name.

It was on Sheer Thursday,
　And all in the morning,
They plaited a crown of thorns
　For our heavenly king:
　　And was not this a woeful thing?
　　And sweet Jesus we'll call him by name.

It was on Good Friday,
　And all in the morning,
They crucified our Saviour,
　And our heavenly king:
　　And was not this a woeful thing?
　　And sweet Jesus we'll call him by name.

It was on Easter Day,
　And all in the morning,
Our Saviour arose,
　Our own heavenly king:
　　The sun and the moon they did both rise with
　　　him,
　　And sweet Jesus we'll call him by name.

AS JOSEPH WAS A-WALKING

As Joseph was a-walking
  He heard Angels sing,
'This night shall be born
  Our Heavenly King.'

'He neither shall be born
  In house nor in hall,
Nor in the place of paradise,
  But in an ox-stall.'

'He shall not be clothèd
  In purple nor pall;
But all in fair linen,
  As wear babies all.'

'He shall not be rockèd
  In silver nor gold,
But in a wooden cradle
  That rocks on the mould.'

'He neither shall be christened
  In milk nor in wine,
But in pure spring-well water
  Fresh spring from Bethine.'

Mary took her baby,
    She dressed him so sweet,
She laid him in a manger,
    All there for to sleep.

As she stood over him
    She heard Angels sing,
'Oh, bless our dear Saviour
    Our Heavenly King!'

A BEETLE

Wee man o' leather
Gaed through the heather,
Through a rock, through a reel,
Through an old spinning-wheel,
Through a sheep-shank bone.
Such a man was never seen.

BEFORE THE PALING OF THE STARS

Before the paling of the stars,
    Before the winter morn,
Before the earliest cock crow,
    Jesus Christ was born:
Born in a stable,
    Cradled in a manger,
In the world his hands had made
    Born a stranger.

Priest and king lay fast asleep
    In Jerusalem;
Young and old lay fast asleep
    In crowded Bethlehem;
Saint and angel, ox and ass,
    Kept a watch together
Before the Christmas daybreak
    In the winter weather.

Jesus on his mother's breast
    In the stable cold,
Spotless lamb of God was he,
    Shepherd of the fold:
Let us kneel with Mary maid,
    With Joseph bent and hoary,
With saint and angel, ox and ass,
    To hail the King of Glory.

CHRISTINA ROSSETTI

BETTY AND HER DUCKS

Oh Betty, Betty, have you seen my ducks to-day?
    Where, boy, where?
All in that yonder pond.
    There, boy, there!

Betty and her ducks.
    Ducks and Betty.
Oliver and her deer.
    Deer and Oliver.

Roland and Oliver,
  The king and the king his deer,
    Now and for ever more.

Oh Thomas, Thomas, have you seen my horse to-day?
  Where, boy, where?
All on that yonder plain.
  There, boy, there!

Thomas and his horse.
  Horse and Thomas.
Betty and her ducks.
  Ducks and Betty . . .
                   (Go on as before.)

Oh Agnes, Agnes, have you seen my geese to-day?
  Where, boy, where?
All on that yonder common.
  There, boy, there!

Agnes and her geese.
  Geese and Agnes.
Thomas and his horse.
  Horse and Thomas.
Betty and her ducks . . .

Oh huntsman, huntsman, have you seen my hounds
    to-day?
  Where, boy, where?
All in that yonder cover.
  There, boy, there!

Huntsman and his hounds.
  Hounds and huntsman.
Agnes and her geese . . .

BIRDS

The peacock is silver,
The eagle is gold,
The wren is a stranger,
The robin is bold.
The dove is a neighbour,
The blue-tit a guest,
The swallow's a traveller
And the owl a ghost.
The crow is black
For the great fields of snow,
And the swan is sailing
For the lakes of to-morrow.

ELENA FEARN

BOBBY SHAFTOE

Bobby Shaftoe's gone to sea,
Silver buckles on his knee;
He'll come back and marry me,
Bonny Bobby Shaftoe.

Bobby Shaftoe's tall and slim,
He's always dressed so neat and trim,
The lassies they all keek at him,
   Bonny Bobby Shaftoe.

Bobby Shaftoe's bright and fair,
Combing down his yellow hair;
He's my ain for ever mair,
   Bonny Bobby Shaftoe.

BONIFACE

Old Boniface he loved good cheer,
   And took his glass of Burton,
And when the nights grew sultry hot
   He slept without a shirt on.

THE BROWN OWL

The Brown Owl sits in the ivy-bush,
   And she looketh wondrous wise,
With a horny beak beneath her cowl.
   And a pair of large, round eyes.

She sat all day on the self-same spray,
   From sunrise to sunset;
And a dim grey light which was all too bright
   For the owl to see in yet.

'Jenny Owlet, Jenny Owlet,' said a merry little bird,
   'They say you're wondrous wise;
But I don't think you see, though you're looking at me
   With your large, round, shining eyes.'

But night came soon, and the pale white moon
   Rolled high up in the skies;
And the great Brown Owl flew away in her cowl.
   With her large, round, shining eyes.

CA' HAWKIE
(*Northumbrian Folk Song*)

Hawkie is a bonny cow
   Though she winna wade the watter,
While she waits the work'll stand,
   Ca'* Hawkie through the watter.

       * Call.

Ca' Hawkie, ca' Hawkie,
    Ca' Hawkie through the watter.
Hawkie is a sweir* beast,
    And Hawkie winna wade the watter.

Hawkie is a pretty cow;
    All the children do adore her,
For she gives them all the milk,
    There is none they prize before her.
    Ca' Hawkie ...

Now, young maids, my counsel take,
    Since that it can be no better;
Cast off baith your hose and shoon,
    Safely drive her through the watter.
    Ca' Hawkie ...

                    * Stubborn.

DAWN

The thrush is tapping a stone
With a snail's shell in its beak;
A small bird hangs from a cherry
Until the stem shall break.
No waking song has begun,
And yet birds chatter and hurry
And throng in the elm's gloom,
Because an owl goes home.

GORDON BOTTOMLEY

THE DEAF WOMAN

'Old woman, old woman, are you fond of smoking?
Old woman, old woman, are you fond of smoking?'
'Speak a little louder, sir, I'm rather hard of hearing.
Speak a little louder, sir, I'm rather hard of hearing.'

'Old woman, old woman, are you fond of carding?
Old woman, old woman, are you fond of carding?'
'Speak a little louder, sir, I'm rather hard of hearing.
Speak a little louder, sir, I'm rather hard of hearing.'

'Old woman, old woman, will you let me court you?
Old woman, old woman, will you let me court you?'
'Speak a little louder, sir, I just begin to hear you.
Speak a little louder, sir, I just begin to hear you.'

'Old woman, old woman, don't you want to marry me?
Old woman, old woman, don't you want to marry me?'
'Lord have mercy on my soul! I think that now I hear you.
Lord have mercy on my soul! I think that now I hear you.'

THE DERBY RAM

As I went down to Derby town,
    'Twas on a market day,
And there I met the finest ram
    Was ever fed on hay.
        Riddle to my rye,
        Riddle to my rye.

The wool upon this ram's back,
　　It grew up to the sky;
The eagles build their nests in it,
　　I heard the young ones cry.
　　　Riddle to my rye,
　　　Riddle to my rye.

The horns upon this ram's head,
　　They grew up to the moon.
A man climbed up in April
　　And never came down till June.
　　　Riddle to my rye,
　　　Riddle to my rye.

The wool upon this ram's tail
　　Was very fine and thin,
Took all the girls in Derby town
　　Full seven years to spin.
　　　Riddle to my rye,
　　　Riddle to my rye.

This ram he had four mighty feet
    And on them he did stand,
And every foot that he had got
    Did cover an acre of land.
      Riddle to my rye,
      Riddle to my rye.

And every tooth this ram had
    Was hollow as a horn.
They took one out and measured it.
    It held a barrel of corn.
      Riddle to my rye,
      Riddle to my rye.

And if you don't believe me
    And think it is a lie,
Then you go down to Derby town
    And see as well as I.
      Riddle to my rye,
      Riddle to my rye.

THE DESERTED HOUSE

There's no smoke in the chimney,
    And the rain beats on the floor;
There's no glass in the window,
    There's no wood in the door;
The heather grows behind the house,
    And the sand lies before.

No hand hath trained the ivy,
  The walls are grey and bare;
The boats upon the sea sail by,
  Nor ever tarry there.
No beast of the field comes nigh,
  Nor any bird of the air.

MARY COLERIDGE

A DIRTY OLD MAN

Who are you? A dirty old man.
I've always been so since the day I began.
Mother and Father were dirty before me.
Hot or cold water has never come o'er me.

DOCTOR FELL

I do not love thee, Doctor Fell:
The reason why I cannot tell,
But this I know, I know full well,
I do not love thee, Doctor Fell...

THE DOVE AND THE WREN

The dove says Coo, coo, what shall I do?
I can scarce maintain two.
Pooh pooh, says the wren, I have got ten,
And keep them all like gentlemen!

A DREAM

What did I dream? I do not know:
　　The fragments fly like chaff.
Yet, strange, my mind was tickled so,
　　I cannot help but laugh.

THE FAIRIES

If ye will with Mab find grace,
Set each platter in his place:
Rake the fire up and get
Water in, ere sun be set.
Wash your pails and cleanse your dairies;
Sluts are loathsome to the fairies:
Sweep your house: who doth not so,
Mab will pinch her by the toe.

ROBERT HERRICK

THE FARMER'S DAUGHTERS

A farmer he lived in the West country,
　　With a hey down, bow down!
A farmer he lived in the West country,
And he had daughters one, two, and three,
　　Singing, I will be true to my love
　　If my love will be true to me.

135

One day they walked by the river's brim,
With a hey down, bow down!
One day they walked by the river's brim
And the eldest pushed the youngest in,
Singing, I will be true to my love
If my love will be true to me.

'O sister, O sister, pray lend me your hand,
With a hey down, bow down!
O sister, O sister, pray lend me your hand,
And I will give thee both house and land,'
Singing, I will be true to my love
If my love will be true to me.

'I'll neither lend you hand nor glove,
With a hey down, bow down!
I'll neither lend you hand nor glove,
Unless you promise me your true love,'
Singing, I will be true to my love
If my love will be true to me.

So down the river the maiden swam,
With a hey down, bow down!
So down the river the maiden swam,
Until she came to the miller's dam,
Singing, I will be true to my love
If my love will be true to me.

The miller's daughter she stood at the door,
With a hey down, bow down!
The miller's daughter she stood at the door,
Blooming like a gillyflower,
Singing, I will be true to my love
If my love will be true to me.

'O father, O father, here swims a swan,
With a hey down, bow down!
O father, O father, here swims a swan,
Very much like a drownded gentlewoman,'
Singing, I will be true to my love
If my love will be true to me.

The miller he took his rod and hook,
With a hey down, bow down!
The miller he took his rod and hook,
And he fished the fair maid out of the brook,
Singing, I will be true to my love
If my love will be true to me.

FIRE DOWN BELOW

Fire in the galley, fire down below;
It's fetch a bucket o' water, girls, there's fire down
below.
Fire! Fire! fire down below,
It's fetch a bucket o' water, girls, there's fire down below.

Fire in the forepeak, fire down below;
It's fetch a bucket o' water girls, there's fire down
below.
Fire! Fire! fire down below,
It's fetch a bucket o' water, girls, there's fire down below.

Fire in the windlass, fire in the chain;
It's fetch a bucket o' water, girls, there's fire down
below.
Fire! Fire! fire down below,
It's fetch a bucket o' water, girls, there's fire down below.

Fire up aloft, and fire down below;
It's fetch a bucket o' water, girls, there's fire down
below.
Fire! Fire! fire down below,
It's fetch a bucket o' water, girls, there's fire down below.

My father died, and I cannot tell how,
He left me six horses to follow the plough.
CHORUS.   *With a wing-wang-waddle, oh!*
            Jack sold his saddle, oh!
            Blossy boys, bubble oh! under the broom.

I sold my six horses and bought me a cow,
I'd fain have a fortune, but didn't know how.
CHORUS. *With a wing-wang-waddle, oh! . . .*

I sold me a cow and bought me a calf,
I'd fain have a fortune, but I lost a half.
CHORUS.   *With a wing-wang-waddle, oh! . . .*

I sold my calf and bought me a cat;
The pretty thing by my chimney sat.
CHORUS.   *With a wing-wang-waddle, oh! . . .*

I sold my cat and I bought me a mouse;
He fired his tail and he burnt down my house.
CHORUS.   *With a wing-wang-waddle, oh! . . .*

I have nothing to buy and I've nothing to sell,
And how I shall live, I'm sure I can't tell.
CHORUS.   *With a wing-wang-waddle, oh! . . .*

THE FROG AND THE CROW

A jolly fat frog did in the river swim, O.
A comely black crow lived on the river brim, O.
'Come on shore, come on shore,' said the crow to the
    frog, and then, O.
'No, you'll bite me; no, you'll bite me,' said the frog
    to the crow again, O.

'Oh, there is sweet music on yonder green hill, O,
And you shall be a dancer, a dancer in yellow.
All in yellow, all in yellow,' said the crow to the frog,
    and then, O,
'All in yellow, all in yellow,' said the frog to the crow
    again, O.

'Farewell, ye little fishes, that in the river swim, O.
I go to be a dancer, a dancer in yellow.'
'Oh, beware; oh, beware,' said the fish to the frog and
    then, O.
'I'll take care, I'll take care,' said the frog to the fish
    again, O.

The frog began a-swimming, a-swimming to land, O.
The crow began a-hopping to give him his hand, O.
'Sir, you're welcome; sir, you're welcome,' said the
    crow to the frog, and then, O,
'Sir, I thank you; sir, I thank you,' said the frog to the
    crow again, O.

'But where is the music on yonder green hill, O?
And where are all the dancers, the dancers in yellow?
All in yellow, all in yellow,' said the frog to the crow,
    and then, O –
But he chuckled, oh he chuckled, and then, O, and then,
    O!

THE FROG AND THE MOUSE

There was a frog lived in a well,
   Whipsee diddledee dandy dee.
There was a mouse lived in a mill,
   Whipsee diddledee dandy dee.
This frog he would a-wooing ride,
With sword and buckler by his side.
   With a harum scarum diddle dum darum,
   Whipsee diddledee dandy dee!

He rode till he came to mouse's hall,
   Whipsee diddledee dandy dee.
Where he most tenderly did call:
   Whipsee diddledee dandy dee.

'Oh, Mistress Mouse, are you at home?
And if you are, oh pray come down.'
    With a harum scarum diddle dum darum,
    Whipsee diddledee dandy dee!

'My uncle Rat is not at home;
    Whipsee diddledee dandy dee.
I dare not for my life come down.'
    Whipsee diddledee dandy dee.
Then Uncle Rat he soon comes home,
'And who's been here since I've been gone?'
    With a harum scarum diddle dum darum,
    Whipsee diddledee dandy dee!

'Here's been a fine young gentleman,
    Whipsee diddledee dandy dee.
Who swears he'll have me if he can.'
    Whipsee diddledee dandy dee.
Then Uncle Rat gave his consent,
And made a handsome settlement.
    With a harum scarum diddle dum darum,
    Whipsee diddledee dandy dee!

Four partridge pies with season made,
    Whipsee diddledee dandy dee,
Two potted larks and marmalade,
    Whipsee diddledee dandy dee,
Four woodcocks and a venison pie —
I would that at that feast were I!
    With a harum scarum diddle dum darum,
    Whipsee diddledee dandy dee!

FROM A RAILWAY CARRIAGE

Faster than fairies, faster than witches,
Bridges and houses, hedges and ditches,
And charging along like troops in a battle,
All through the meadows the horses and cattle:
All of the sights of the hill and the plain
Fly as thick as driving rain;
And ever again, in the wink of an eye,
Painted stations whistle by.

Here is a child who clambers and scrambles,
All by himself and gathering brambles;
Here is a tramp who stands and gazes;
And there is the green for stringing the daisies!
Here is a cart run away in the road,
Lumping along with man and load;
And here is a mill, and there is a river;
Each a glimpse and gone for ever!

ROBERT LOUIS STEVENSON

GOD MADE THE BEES

God made the bees,
   And the bees make honey.
The miller's man does all the work,
   But the miller makes the money.

GREEN BROOM

There was an old man lived out in the wood,
   His trade was a-cutting of Broom, green Broom;
He had but one son without thrift, without good,
   Who lay in his bed till 'twas noon, bright noon.

The old man awoke, one morning and spoke;
   He swore he would fire the room, that room,
If his John would not rise and open his eyes,
   And away to the wood to cut Broom, green Broom.

So Johnny arose, and he slipped on his clothes,
   And away to the wood to cut Broom, green Broom;
He sharpened his knives, for once he contrives
   To cut a great bundle of Broom, green Broom;

When Johnny passed under a lady's fine house,
   Passed under a lady's fine room, fine room,
She called to her maid, 'Go fetch me,' she said,
   'Go fetch me the boy that sells Broom, green Broom.'

When Johnny came into the lady's fine house,
   And stood in the lady's fine room, fine room,
'Young Johnny,' she said, 'will you give up your trade,
   And marry a lady in bloom, full bloom?'

Johnny gave his consent, and to church they both went,
And he wedded the lady in bloom, full bloom;
At market and fair, all folks do declare,
   There is none like the Boy that sold Broom, green
   Broom.

HENRY AND MARY

Henry was a young king,
   Mary was a queen;
He gave her a snowdrop
   On a stalk of green.

All for his kindness
   And all for his care
She gave him a new-laid egg
   In the garden there.

'Love, can you sing?'
               'I cannot sing.'
  'Or tell a tale?'
                'Not one I know.'
'Then let us play at queen and king
   As down the garden walks we go.'

ROBERT GRAVES

HENRY MARTYN

In merry Scotland, in merry Scotland
   There lived brothers three;
They all did cast lots which of them should go
   A-robbing upon the salt sea.

The lot it fell on Henry Martyn,
   The youngest of the three;
That he should go rob on the salt, salt sea,
   To maintain his brothers and he.

He had not sailed a long winter's night,
   Nor yet a short winter's day,
Before that he met with a lofty old ship,
   Come sailing along that way.

'Stand off! stand off!' said Henry Martyn,
   'For you shall not pass by me;
For I am a robber all on the salt seas,
   To maintain us brothers three.'

'Stand off! stand off!' the captain he cried,
   'The life-guards they are aboard.
My cannons are loaden with powder and shot;
   And every man hath a sword.'

For three long hours they merrily fought,
   For hours they fought full three;
At last a deep wound got Henry Martyn,
   And down by the mast fell he.

'Twas broadside against a broadside then,
   And at it the which should win,
A shot in the gallant ship bored a hole,
   And then did the water rush in.

Bad news, bad news for old England,
   Bad news has come to the town,
For a rich merchant's vessel is cast away
   And all her brave seamen drown.

Bad news, bad news through the London street,
   Bad news has come to the King!
The lives of his guard they be all a-lost,
   O the tidings be sad that I bring.

THE HERRING LOVES

The herring loves the merry moonlight,
   The mackerel loves the wind;
But the oyster loves the dredging song,
   For she comes of a gentle kind.

HIS HIGHNESS' DOG

(engraved on a dog's collar)

I am his Highness' dog at Kew;
Pray tell me, sir, whose dog are you?

ALEXANDER POPE

HUNTING SONG

Up, up! ye dames, and lasses gay!
To the meadows trip away.
'Tis you must tend the flocks this morn,
And scare the small birds from the corn.
    Not a soul at home must stay;
        For the shepherds must go
        With lance and bow
    To hunt the wolf in the woods to-day.

Leave the hearth and leave the house
To the cricket and the mouse:
Find the grannam out a sunny seat
With babe and lambkin at her feet.
    Not a soul at home must stay:
        For the shepherds must go
        With lance and bow
    To hunt the wolf in the woods to-day.

SAMUEL TAYLOR COLERIDGE

I WENT TO NOKE

I went to Noke,
But nobody spoke;
I went to Thame,
It was just the same;
Burford and Brill
Were silent and still;
But I went to Beckley
And they spoke directly.

I WILL LIFT UP MINE EYES

I will lift up mine eyes unto the hills, from whence
cometh my help. My help cometh from the Lord, which
made Heaven and earth.

He will not suffer thy foot to be moved: he that keepeth
thee will not slumber. Behold, he that keepeth Israel
shall neither slumber nor sleep.

The Lord is thy keeper: the Lord is thy shade upon
thy right hand.

The sun shall not smite thee by day, nor the moon by night. The Lord shall preserve thee from evil: he shall preserve thy soul.

The Lord shall preserve thy going out and thy coming in from this time forth, and even for evermore.

PSALM 121

IS THE MOON TIRED?

Is the moon tired? She looks so pale
    Within her misty veil;
She scales the sky from east to west,
    And takes no rest.

Before the coming of the night
    The moon shows papery white;
Before the dawning of the day
    She fades away.

CHRISTINA ROSSETTI

IT WAS A LOVER AND HIS LASS

It was a lover and his lass,
    With a hey and a ho and a hey nonny no!
That o'er the green corn-field did pass
    In the spring time, the only pretty ring time,
        When birds do sing
        Hey ding-a-ding ding!
    Sweet lovers love the spring.

Between the acres of the rye,
  With a hey and a ho and a hey nonny no!
These pretty country folks would lie,
  In the spring time . . .

This carol they began that hour,
  With a hey and a ho and a hey nonny no!
How that a life was but a flower
  In the spring time . . .

And therefore take the present time,
  With a hey and a ho and a hey nonny no!
For love is crownèd with the prime
  In the spring time . . .

                        WILLIAM SHAKESPEARE

THE JOLLY MILLER

There was a jolly miller once
  Lived on the River Dee.
He worked so hard from morn till night,
  No lark so blithe as he.

And this the burden of his song
  For ever used to be,
'I care for nobody, no, not I,
  If nobody cares for me.'

KITTY ALONE

There was frog lived in a well,
  Kitty alone, Kitty alone;
There was a frog lived in a well,
  Kitty alone and I.
There was a frog lived in a well,
And a merry mouse in a mill.
  Cock me cary, Kitty alone,
  Kitty alone and I.

This frog he would a-wooing ride,
  Kitty alone . . .
This frog he would a-wooing ride,
  Kitty alone and I.
This frog he would a-wooing ride,
And on a snail he got astride,
  Cock me cary . . .

He rode till he came to my Lady Mouse Hall,
  Kitty alone . . .
He rode till he came to my Lady Mouse Hall,
  Kitty alone and I.
He rode till he came to my Lady Mouse Hall,
And there he did both knock and call.
  Cock me cary . . .

Quoth he, 'Miss Mouse, I'm come to thee,'
Kitty alone . . .
Quoth he, 'Miss Mouse, I'm come to thee,'
Kitty alone and I.
Quoth he, 'Miss Mouse, I'm come to thee,
To see if thou canst fancy me.'
Cock me cary . . .

Quoth she, 'Answer I'll give you none,'
Kitty alone . . .
Quoth she, 'Answer I'll give you none,'
Kitty alone and I.
Quoth she, 'Answer I'll give you none,
Until my Uncle Rat comes home.'
Cock me cary . . .

And when her Uncle Rat came home,
Kitty alone . . .
And when her Uncle Rat came home,
Kitty alone and I.
And when her Uncle Rat came home:
'Who's been here since I've been gone?'
Cock me cary . . .

'Sir, there's been a worthy gentleman,'
Kitty alone . . .
'Sir there's been a worthy gentleman,'
Kitty alone and I.
'Sir, there's been a worthy gentleman,
Has been here since you've been gone.'
Cock me cary . . .

The frog he came whistling through the brook,
  Kitty alone . . .
The frog he came whistling through the brook,
  Kitty alone and I.
The frog he came whistling through the brook,
And there he met with a dainty duck.
  Cock me cary . . .

This duck she swallowed him up with a cluck,
  Kitty alone . . .
This duck she swallowed him up with a cluck,
  Kitty alone and I.
This duck she swallowed him up with a cluck,
So there's an end of my history-book.
  Cock me cary . . .

MY AUNT

My aunt she died a month ago,
  And left me all her riches,
A feather-bed and a wooden leg,
  And a pair of calico breeches;
A coffee-pot without a spout,
  And a mug without a handle,
A baccy box without a lid,
  And half a farden candle!

A NAUGHTY BOY

(*from* A Song about Myself)

There was a naughty boy,
   And a naughty boy was he,
He ran away to Scotland,
   The people there to see —
   Then he found
   That the ground
   Was as hard,
   That a yard
   Was as long,
   That a song
   Was as merry,
   That a cherry
   Was as red,
   That lead
   Was as weighty,
   That fourscore
   Was as eighty,
   That a door
   Was as wooden
   As in England —
So he stood in his shoes
   And he wondered,
   He wondered,
He stood in his shoes
   And he wondered.

JOHN KEATS

NEEDLES AND RIBBONS

Needles and ribbons and packets of pins,
Prints and chintz and odd bod-a-kins —
   They'd never mind whether
   You laid them together
Or one from the other in pockets and tins.

But packets of pins and ribbons and needles
And odd bod-a-kins and chintz and prints,
   Being birds of a feather
   Would huddle together
Like minnows on billows or pennies in mints.

OH, THAT I WAS

Oh, that I was where I would be!
Then would I be where I am not!
But where I am, I must be,
And where I would be I cannot.

THE OLD LADY OF CHERTSEY

There was an old lady of Chertsey,
Who made a remarkable curtsey;
   She twirled round and round,
   Till she sunk underground,
Which distressed all the people of Chertsey.

EDWARD LEAR

THE OLD MAN IN A BARGE

There was an old man in a barge,
Whose nose was exceedingly large;
    But in fishing by night,
    It supported a light,
Which helped that old man in a barge.

EDWARD LEAR

THE OLD MAN OF THERMOPYLAE

There was an Old Man of Thermopylae,
Who never did anything properly;
    But they said, 'If you choose
    To boil Eggs in your Shoes,
You shall never remain in Thermopylae.'

EDWARD LEAR

THE OLD TAILOR

There was once an old Tailor of Hickery Mo,
Too tired at evening to sew, to sew:
He put by his needle, he snapped his thread,
And, cross-legged, sang to his fiddle instead.
His candle bobbed at each note that came
And spat out a spark from the midst of its flame:

His catgut strings they yelped and yawled,
The wilder their scrapings the louder he bawled;
The grease strickled over at every beat,
Welled down to the stick in a winding-sheet —
Till up sprang puss from the fire, with a *WOW*!
'A *fine* kakkamangul you're making now!'

WALTER DE LA MARE

POOR OLD HORSE

My clothing was once of the linsey woolsey fine,
My tail it grew at length, my coat did likewise shine;
But now I'm growing old; my beauty does decay,
My master frowns upon me; one day I heard him say,
　　　　　Poor old horse: poor old horse.

Once I was kept in the stable snug and warm,
To keep my tender limbs from any cold or harm;
But now, in open fields, I am forced for to go,
In all sorts of weather, let it be hail, rain, freeze or snow.
　　　　　Poor old horse: poor old horse.

Once I was fed on the very best corn and hay
That ever grew in yon fields, or in yon meadows gay;
But now there's no such doing can I find at all,
I'm glad to pick the green sprouts that grow behind yon
    wall.

                 Poor old horse: poor old horse.

'You are old, you are cold, you are deaf, dull, dumb and
    slow,
You are not fit for anything, or in my team to draw.
You have eaten all my hay, you have spoiled all my straw.
So hang him, whip, stick him, to the huntsman let him
    go.'

                 Poor old horse: poor old horse.

My hide unto the tanners then I would freely give,
My body to the hound dogs, I would rather die than live,
Likewise my poor old bones that have carried you many a
    mile,
Over hedges, ditches, brooks, bridges, likewise gates and
    stiles.

                 Poor old horse: poor old horse.

PRAISE THE LORD

Praise the Lord from the earth, ye dragons, and all deeps: fire, and hail; snow, and vapours; stormy wind fulfilling his word:

Mountains, and all hills; fruitful trees, and all cedars:

Beasts, and all cattle; creeping things, and flying fowl:

Kings of the earth, and all people; princes, and all judges of the earth:

Both young men, and maidens; old men, and children:

Let them praise the name of the Lord.

from PSALM 148

QUACK!

The duck is whiter than whey is,
　His tail tips up over his back,
The eye in his head is as round as a button,
　　And he says, *Quack! Quack!*

He swims on his bright blue mill-pond,
　By the willow-tree under the shack,
Then stands on his head to see down to the bottom,
　　And says, *Quack! Quack!*

When Molly steps out of the kitchen,
　For apron—pinned round with a sack;
He squints at her round face, her dish, and what's in it,
　　And says, *Quack! Quack!*

160

He preens the pure snow of his feathers
In the sun by the wheat-straw stack;
At dusk waddles home with his brothers and sisters,
And says, *Quack! Quack!*

WALTER DE LA MARE

THE QUANGLE WANGLE'S HAT

On top of the Crumpetty Tree
The Quangle Wangle sat,
But his face you could not see,
On account of his Beaver Hat.
For his Hat was a hundred and two feet wide,
With ribbons and bibbons on every side,
And bells, and buttons, and loops, and lace,
So that nobody ever could see the face
Of the Quangle Wangle Quee.

The Quangle Wangle said
To himself on the Crumpetty Tree,
'Jam; and jelly; and bread;
Are the best of food for me!
But the longer I live on this Crumpetty Tree,
The plainer than ever it seems to me
That very few people come this way,
And that life on the whole is far from gay!'
Said the Quangle Wangle Quee.

But there came to the Crumpetty Tree
Mr and Mrs Canary;
And they said, 'Did ever you see
Any spot so charmingly airy?

May we build a nest on your lovely Hat?
Mr Quangle Wangle, grant us that!
O please let us come and build a nest
Of whatever material suits you best,
    Mr Quangle Wangle Quee!'

And besides, to the Crumpetty Tree
    Came the Stork, the Duck, and the Owl;
The Snail and the Bumble-Bee,
    The Frog, and the Fimble Fowl
(The Fimble Fowl with a corkscrew leg);
And all of them said, 'We humbly beg,
We may build our homes on your lovely Hat,
Mr Quangle Wangle, grant us that!
    Mr Quangle Wangle Quee!'

And the Golden Grouse came there,
    And the Pobble who hast no toes,
And the small Olympian Bear
    And the Dong with a luminous nose.
And the Blue Baboon, who played the flute,
And the Orient Calf from the Land of Tute,
And the Attery Squash and the Bisky Bat,
All came and built on the lovely Hat
    Of the Quangle Wangle Quee.

And the Quangle Wangle said
   To himself on the Crumpetty Tree,
'When all these creasures move
   What a wonderful noise there'll be!'
And at night by the light of the Mulberry Moon
They danced to the Flute of the Blue Baboon
On the broad green leaves of the Crumpetty Tree,
And all were as happy as happy could be,
    With the Quangle Wangle Quee.

EDWARD LEAR

THE RED ROBIN

Cock Robin, he got a new tippet in spring,
And he sat in a shed, and heard other birds sing.
And he whistled a ballad as loud as he could,
And built him a nest of oak leaves by the wood,
And finished it just as the celandine pressed
Like a bright burning blaze, by the edge of its nest
All glittering with sunshine and beautiful rays,
Like high polished brass, or the fire in a blaze;
Then sung a new song on the edge of the brere;
And so it kept singing the whole of the year.
Till cowslips and wild roses blossomed and died,
The red robin sang by the old spinney side.

JOHN CLARE

ROBIN HOOD AND LITTLE JOHN

Robin Hood, Robin Hood
Is in the mickle wood!
Little John, Little John,
He to the town is gone.
Robin Hood, Robin Hood
Is telling his beads,
All in the greenwood
Among the green weeds.
Little John, Little John,
If he comes no more,
Robin Hood, Robin Hood,
We shall fret full sore!

ROBIN-A-THRUSH

Oh, Robin-a-Thrush he married a wife,
  With a hoppety, moppety mow now!
She proved to be the plague of his life,
  With a hig-jig-jiggety, ruffety petticoat,
  Robin-a-Thrush cries mow now!

She never gets up till twelve o'clock,
  With a hoppety, moppety mow now!
Puts on her gown and above it her smock.
  With a hig-jig-jiggety . . .

She sweeps the house but once a year,
  With a hoppety, moppety mow now!
The reason is that brooms are dear.
  With a hig-jig-jiggety . . .

She milks her cows but once a week,
  With a hoppety, moppety mow now!
And that's what makes her butter sweet.
  With a hig-jig-jiggety . . .

The butter she made in an old man's boot;
With a hoppety, moppety mow now!
For want of a churn she clapped in her foot.
With a hig-jig-jiggety . . .

Her cheese when made was put on the shelf,
With a hoppety, moppety mow now!
And it never was turned till it turned of itself.
With a hig-jig-jiggety . . .

It turned and turned till it walked on the floor,
With a hoppety, moppety mow now!
It stood upon legs and walked to the door.
With a hig-jig-jiggety . . .

It walked till it came to Banbury Fair;
With a hoppety, moppety mow now!
The dame followed after upon a grey mare.
With a hig-jig-jiggety . . .

This song it was made for gentlemen,
With a hoppety, moppety mow now!
If you want any more you must sing it again!
With a hig-jig-jiggety . . .

THE SONG OF THE WESTERN MEN

A good sword and a trusty hand!
   A merry heart and true!
King James's men shall understand
   What Cornish lads can do.

And have they fixed the where and when?
   And shall Trelawny die?
Here's twenty thousand Cornish men
   Will know the reason why!

Out spake their captain brave and bold,
   A merry wight was he:
'If London Tower were Michael's hold,
   We'll set Trelawny free!

'We'll cross the Tamar, land to land,
   The Severn is no stay, –
With "one and all",* and hand in hand,
   And who shall bid us nay?

'And when we come to London Wall,
   A pleasant sight to view,
Come forth! Come forth, ye cowards all,
   Here's men as good as you!

'Trelawny he's in keep and hold,
   Trelawny he may die; –
But here's twenty thousand Cornish bold
   Will know the reason why!'

ROBERT STEPHEN HAWKER

* The motto of Cornwall.

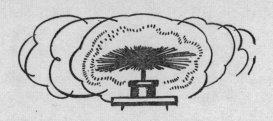

'SOOEEP'

Black as a chimney is his face,
    And ivory white his teeth,
And in his brass-bound cart he rides,
    The chestnut blooms beneath.

'Sooeep, Sooeep!' he cries, and brightly peers
    This way and that, to see
With his two light-blue shining eyes
    What custom there may be.

And once inside the house, he'll squat,
    And drive his rods on high,
Till twirls his sudden sooty brush
    Against the morning sky.

Then 'mid his bulging bags of soot,
    With half the world asleep,
His small cart wheels him off again,
    Still hoarsely bawling, 'Sooeep!'

WALTER DE LA MARE

THREE KNIGHTS FROM SPAIN

'We are three brethren come from Spain,
  All in French garlands;
We are come to court your daughter Jane,
  And adieu to you, my darlings.'

'My daughter Jane! she is too young,
  All in French garlands;
She cannot bide your flattering tongue,
  And adieu to you, my darlings.'

'Be she young, or be she old,
  All in French garlands;
'Tis for a bride she must be sold,
  And adieu to you, my darlings.'

'A bride, a bride she shall not be,
  All in French garlands;
Till she go through this world with me,
  And adieu to you, my darlings.'

'Then shall you keep your daughter Jane,
  All in French garlands;
Come once, and come not here again,
  And adieu to you, my darlings.'

'Turn back, turn back, you Spanish knights,
    All in French garlands;
Scour, scour your spurs till they be bright,
    And adieu to you, my darlings.'

'Sharp shine our spurs, all richly wrought,
    All in French garlands;
In towns afar our spurs were bought,
    And adieu to you, my darlings.'

'Smell my lilies, smell my roses,
    All in French garlands;
Which of my maidens do you choose?
    And adieu to you, my darlings.'

'Not she; not she; thy youngest, Jane!
    All in French garlands;
We ride — and ride not back again,
    And adieu to you, my darlings.'

'In every pocket a thousand pound,
    All in French garlands;
On every finger a gay gold ring,
    And adieu to you, my darlings.'

TOM THUMB'S ALPHABET

A was an Archer who shot at a frog.
B was a Butcher who had a great dog.
C was a Captain all covered with lace.
D was a Drummer who played with a grace.
E was an Esquire with pride on his brow.

F was a Farmer who followed the plough.
G was a Gamester who had but ill luck.
H was a Hunter who hunted a buck.
I was an Italian who had a white mouse.
J was a Joiner who built up a house.
K was a King so mighty and grand.
L was a Lady who had a white hand.
M was a Miser who hoarded up gold.
N was a Nobleman gallant and bold.
O was an Organ boy who played for his bread,
P a Policeman of bad boys the dread.
Q was a Quaker who would not bow down.
R was a Robber who prowled about town.
S was a Sailor who spent all he got.
T was a Tinker who mended a pot.
U was an Usher* with dunces severe.
V was a Veteran who never knew fear.
W was a Waiter with dinners in store.
X was expensive and so became poor.
Y was a Youth who did not like school.
Z was a Zany who looked a great fool.

* Schoolmaster.

A TREE

In Spring I look gay,
Decked in comely array,
In Summer more clothing I wear;
When colder it grows
I fling off my clothes,
And in Winter quite naked appear.

THE TREE ON THE HILL

There was a tree upon a hill,
The finest tree you ever did see,
And the tree was on the hill,
And the hill stood still,
AND —
The green grass grew all around, my boys,
The green grass grew all around.

There was a bough upon that tree,
The finest bough you ever did see,
And the bough was on the tree,
And the tree was on the hill,
And the hill stood still,
AND —
The green grass grew all around, my boys,
The green grass grew all around.

There was a branch upon that bough,
The finest branch you ever did see,
And the branch was on the bough,
And the bough was on the tree,
And the tree . . .
   (*Go on as in previous verses*)

There was a twig upon that branch,
The finest twig you ever did see,
And the twig was on the branch,
And the branch . . .

There was a leaf upon that twig,
The finest leaf you ever did see,

And the leaf was on the twig,
And the twig . . .

There was a nest upon that leaf,
The finest nest you ever did see,
And the nest was on the leaf,
And the leaf . . .

There was a bird upon that nest,
The finest bird you ever did see,
And the bird was on the nest,
And the nest . . .

There was a wing upon that bird,
The finest wing you ever did see,
And the wing was on the bird,
And the bird . . .

There was a feather upon that wing,
The finest feather you ever did see,
And the feather was on the wing,
And the wing was on the bird,
And the bird was on the nest,
And the nest was on the leaf,
And the leaf was on the twig,
And the twig was on the branch,
And the branch was on the bough,
And the bough was on the tree,
And the tree was on the hill,
And the hill stood still,
AND —
The green grass grew all around, my boys,
The green grass grew all around.

TWELVE HUNTSMEN

Twelve huntsmen with horns and hounds,
Hunting over other men's grounds;
Eleven ships sailing o'er the main,
Some bound for France and some for Spain,
I wish them all safe home again;
Ten comets in the sky,
Some low and some high;
Nine peacocks in the air,
I wonder how they all came there,
I do not know and I do not care;
Eight joiners in Joiners' Hall,
Working with the tools and all;
Seven lobsters in a dish,
As fresh as any heart could wish;
Six beetles against the wall,
Close by an old woman's apple-stall;
Five puppies of our dog Ball,
Who daily for their breakfast call;
Four horses stuck in a bog,
Three monkeys tied to a clog;
Two pudding-ends would choke a dog,
With a gaping, wide-mouthed waddling frog.

THE TWO RAVENS

As I was walking all alone,
I heard two ravens making a moan,
The one unto the other say,
'Where shall we go and dine to-day?'

'In behind yon old turf-dyke,
I wot there lies a new-slain knight;
And nobody knows that he lies there,
But his hawk, his hound, and lady fair.

'His hound is to the hunting gone,
His hawk to fetch the wild fowl home,
His lady's taken another mate,
So we may make our dinner sweet.

'Ye'll sit on his white neck-bone
And I'll pick out his bonny blue eyes:
With one lock of his golden hair
We'll thatch our nest when it grows bare.

'Many a one for him makes moan,
But none shall know where he is gone.
O'er his white bones, when they are bare,
The wind shall blow for ever more.'

THE UMBRELLA TREES

Under the umbrageous* umbrella trees
Easily the elephant eats at his ease;
The horn of the hunter is heard on the hill,
And the hounds are a-harking in harmony shrill.

  * Shady.

WE'RE ALL IN THE DUMPS

We're all in the dumps,
  For diamonds are trumps,
The kittens are gone to Saint Paul's,
  The babies are bit,
  The moon's in a fit,
And the houses are built without walls.

WHO HAS SEEN THE WIND?

Who has seen the wind?
Neither I nor you:
But when the leaves hang trembling,
The wind is passing through.

Who has seen the wind?
Neither you nor I:
But when the trees bow down their heads,
The wind is passing by.

CHRISTINA ROSSETTI

THE WIND IN A FROLIC

The wind one morning sprang up from sleep,
Saying, 'Now for a frolic! now for a leap!
Now for a madcap galloping chase!
I'll make a commotion in every place!'

So it swept with a bustle right through a great town,
Cracking the signs and scattering down
Shutters; and whisking with merciless squalls,
Old women's bonnets and gingerbread stalls.

There never was heard a much lustier shout,
As the apples and oranges trundled about;
And the urchins that stand, with their thievish eyes
For ever on watch, ran off each with a prize.

Then away to the fields it went blustering and humming,
And the cattle all wondered what monster was coming.
It plucked by the tails the grave matronly cows,
And tossed the colts' manes all over their brows;
Till, offended at such an unusual salute,
They all turned their backs and stood sulky and mute.

So on it went, capering and playing its pranks, —
Whistling with reeds on the broad river's banks,
Puffing the birds as they sat on the spray,
Or the traveller grave on the King's highway.
It was not too nice to hustle the bags
Of the beggar, and flutter his dirty rags;
'Twas so bold that it feared not to play its joke
With the doctor's wig or the gentleman's cloak.

Through the forest it roared, and cried gaily, 'Now,
You sturdy old oaks, I'll make you bow!'
And it made them bow without more ado,
For it cracked their great branches through and through.

Then it rushed like a monster on cottage and farm,
Striking their dwellers with sudden alarm;
And they ran out like bees in a mid-summer swarm;
There were dames with their kerchiefs tied over their
    caps,
To see if their poultry were free from mishaps;

The turkeys they gobbled, the geese screamed aloud,
And the hens crept to roost in a terrified crowd;
There was rearing of ladders, and logs were laid on,
Where the thatch from the roof threatened soon to be
    gone.

But the wind had swept on, and had met in a lane
With a schoolboy, who panted and struggled in vain;
For it tossed him and twirled him, then passed – and he
   stood
With his hat in a pool, and shoes in the mud!

Then away went the wind in its holiday glee,
And now it was far on the billowy sea:
And the lordly ships felt its staggering blow,
And the little boats darted to and fro.

But, lo! it was night, and it sank to rest
On the sea-bird's rock in the gleaming west,
Laughing to think, in its frolicsome fun,
How little of mischief it really had done.

WILLIAM HOWITT

THE WOOD OF FLOWERS

I went to the wood of flowers,
   (No one was with me)
I was there alone for hours –
   I was happy as could be
In the wood of flowers.

There was grass on the ground,
   There were buds on the tree,
And the wind had a sound
   Of such gaiety,
That I was as happy
   As happy could be,
In the wood of flowers.

JAMES STEPHENS

THE WRAGGLE TAGGLE GYPSIES

Three gypsies stood at the Castle gate,
   They sang so high, they sang so low,
The lady sate in her chamber late,
   Her heart it melted away as snow.

They sang so sweet, they sang so shrill,
   That fast her tears began to flow.
And she laid down her silken gown,
   Her golden rings and all her show.

She plucked off her high-heeled shoes,
   A-made of Spanish leather, O!
She would in the street, with her bare, bare feet,
   All out in the wind and weather, O!

It was late last night, when my lord came home,
Enquiring for his a-lady, O!
The servants said on every hand,
'She's gone with the wraggle taggle gypsies, O!'

'O saddle to me my milk-white steed.
Go and fetch me my pony, O!
That I may ride and seek my bride,
Who is gone with the wraggle taggle gypsies, O!'

O he rode high and he rode low,
He rode through woods and copses too.
Until he came to an open field,
And there he espied his a-lady, O!

'What makes you leave your house and land?
What makes you leave your money, O?
What makes you leave your new-wedded lord,
To go with the wraggle taggle gypsies, O?'

'What care I for my house and my land?
What care I for my money, O?
What care I for my new-wedded lord?
I'm off with the wraggle taggle gypsies, O!'

'Last night you slept on a goose-feather bed,
With the sheet turned down so bravely, O!
And to-night you'll sleep in a cold open field,
Along with the wraggle taggle gypsies, O!'

'What care I for a goose-feather bed,
With the sheet turned down so bravely, O?
For to-night I shall sleep in a cold open field,
Along with the wraggle taggle gypsies, O!'

PART FOUR

STRAWBERRY FAIR

AEIOU

We are very little creatures,
All of different voice and features;
One of us in glass is set,
One of us you'll find in jet.
T'other you may see in tin,
And the fourth a box within.
If the fifth you should pursue,
It can never fly from you.

JONATHAN SWIFT

ALLIE

Allie, call the birds in,
    The birds from the sky!
Allie calls, Allie sings,
    Down they all fly:
First there came
Two white doves,
    A sparrow from his nest,
Then a clucking bantam hen,
    Then a robin red-breast.

Allie, call the beasts in,
    The beasts, every one!
Allie calls, Allie sings,
    In they all run:
First there came
Two black lambs,
    Then a grunting Berkshire sow,
Then a dog without a tail,
    Then a red and white cow.

Allie, call the fish up,
   The fish from the stream!
Allie calls, Allie sings,
   Up they all swim:
First there came
Two gold fish,
   A minnow and a miller's thumb,
Then a school of little trout,
   Then the twisting eels come.

Allie, call the children,
   Call them from the green!
Allie calls, Allie sings,
   Soon they run in:
First there came
Tom and Madge,
   Kate and I who'll not forget
How we played by the water's edge
   Till the April sun set.

ROBERT GRAVES

AS I WALKED BY MYSELF

As I walked by myself,
And talked to myself,
   Myself said unto me,
'Look to thyself,
Take care of thyself,
   For nobody cares for thee.'

I answered myself,
And said to myself,
   In the self-same way to me,

'Look to thyself
Or not look to thyself,
    The self-same thing will be.'

AY ME, ALAS, HEIGH HO!

Ay me, alas, heigh ho, heigh ho!
Thus doth Messalina go
Up and down the house a-crying,
For her monkey lies a-dying.
Death, thou art too cruel
To bereave her of her jewel,
Or to make a seizure
Of her only treasure.
If her monkey die,
She will sit and cry,
Fie, fie, fie, fie, fie!

A BED

Formed long ago, yet made to-day,
    Employed while others sleep;
What few would like to give away,
    Nor any wish to keep.

THE BIG BABOON

The Big Baboon is found upon
    The plains of Cariboo:
He goes about with nothing on
    (A shocking thing to do).

But if he dressed respectably
　And let his whiskers grow,
How like this Big Baboon would be
　To Mr So-and-so!

HILAIRE BELLOC

BUY BROOM BUZZUMS

(*Northumbrian Folk Song*)

If you want a buzzum
For to sweep your hoose,
Come to me, maw hinnies,*
Ye may ha' your choose.
　Buy broom buzzums,
　　Buy them when they're new,
　Fine heather-bred 'uns,
　　Better never grew.

* My honeys.

If Aw had a horse
Aw wad hev a cairt;
If Aw had a wife
She wad tyek me pairt.*
   Buy broom buzzums ...

Had Aw but a wife,
Aw care not what she be,
If she's but a woman
That's enough for me.
   Buy broom buzzums ...

If she liked a droppie
Her and I'd agree,
If she didn't like it
There's the mair for me.
   Buy broom buzzums ...

     * Take my part.

THE CAT

Within that porch, across the way,
  I see two naked eyes this night;
Two eyes that neither shut nor blink,
  Searching my face with a green light.

But cats to me are strange, so strange –
  I cannot sleep if one is near;
And though I'm sure I see those eyes,
  I'm not so sure a body's there!

W. H. DAVIES

CLOCK-A-CLAY

In the cowslip pips I lie,
Hidden from the buzzing fly,
While green grass beneath me lies,
Pearled with dew like fishes' eyes,
Here I lie, a clock-a-clay,*
Waiting for the time of day.

While the forest quakes surprise,
And the wild wind sobs and sighs,
My home ricks are like to fall,
On its pillar green and tall;
When the pattering rain drives by
Clock-a-clay keeps warm and dry.

Day by day and night by night,
All the week I hide from sight;
In the cowslip pips I lie,
In rain and dew still warm and dry;
Day and night, and night and day,
Red, black-spotted clock-a-clay.

My home shakes in wind and showers,
Pale green pillar topped with flowers,
Bending at the wild wind's breath,
Till I touch the grass beneath,
Here I live, lone clock-a-clay,
Watching for the time of day.

JOHN CLARE

* Ladybird.

COME UNTO THESE YELLOW SANDS

Come unto these yellow sands,
   and then take hands:
Curtsied when you have and kissed
   the wild waves whist:
Foot it featly here and there,
And sweet sprites the burden bear.
Hark, hark, bow wow:
   the watch-dogs bark, bow wow.
Hark, hark, I hear
   the strain of strutting Chanticleer
Cry cock-a-diddle dow!

WILLIAM SHAKESPEARE

A COUNTRYMAN'S LIFE

Oh, the sweet contentment
   The countryman doth find,
High trolollie lollie lo, high trolollie lee!
   That quiet contemplation
   Possesseth all my mind:
Then care away, and wend along with me.

Our clothing is good sheepskins,
   Grey russet for our wives,
High trolollie lollie lo, high trolollie lee!
   'Tis warmth and not gay clothing
   That doth prolong our lives:
Then care away, and wend along with me.

The cuckoo and the nightingale
Full merrily do sing,
High trolollie lollie lo, high trolollie lee!
And with their pleasant roundelays
Bid welcome to the spring:
Then care away, and wend along with me.

JOHN CHALKHILL

THE DEATH OF ADMIRAL BENBOW

Come all you seamen bold and draw near, and draw near,
Come all you seamen bold and draw near.
It's of an admiral's fame, O brave Benbow was his name,
How he fought all on the main you shall hear, you shall
    hear.

Brave Benbow he set sail for to fight, for to fight,
Brave Benbow he set sail for to fight;
Brave Benbow he set sail with a fine and pleasant gale,
But his captains they turned tail in a fright, in a fright.

Says Kirby unto Wade, we will run, we will run,
Says Kirby unto Wade, we will run!
For I value no disgrace, not the losing of my place,
But the enemy I won't face nor his guns, nor his guns.

The Ruby and Benbow fought the French, fought the
    French,
The Ruby and Benbow fought the French;
They fought them up and down, till the blood came
    trickling down,
Till the blood came trickling down where they lay, where
    they lay.

Brave Benbow lost his legs by chain-shot, by chain-shot,
Brave Benbow lost his legs by chain-shot:
Brave Benbow lost his legs, and all on his stumps he
    begs —
Fight on, my English lads, 'tis our lot, 'tis our lot.

The surgeon dressed his wounds; cries Benbow, cries
    Benbow:
The surgeon dressed his wounds; cries Benbow —
Let a cradle now in haste on the quarter deck be placed
That the enemy I may face till I die, till I die.

A DREAM

Once a dream did weave a shade
O'er my Angel-guarded bed
That an emmet* lost its way
Where on grass methought I lay.

Troubled, wildered, and forlorn,
Dark, benighted, travel-worn,
Over many a tangled spray,
All heart-broke I heard her say:

'O, my children! do they cry?
Do they hear their father sigh?
Now they look abroad to see:
Now return and weep for me.'

Pitying, I dropped a tear;
But I saw a glow-worm near,

* Ant.

193

Who replied: 'What wailing wight
Calls the watchman of the night?

'I am set to light the ground,
While the beetle goes his round:
Follow now the beetle's hum;
Little wanderer, hie thee home.'

WILLIAM BLAKE

THE ECHOING GREEN

The Sun does arise,
And make happy the skies;
The merry bells ring
To welcome the Spring;
The skylark and thrush,
The birds of the bush,
Sing louder around
To the bells' cheerful sound,
While our sports shall be seen
On the Echoing Green.

Old John, with white hair,
Does laugh away care,
Sitting under the oak,
Among the old folk.
They laugh at our play,
And soon they all say:
'Such, such were the joys
When we all, girls and boys,
In our youth-time were seen
On the Echoing Green.'

Till the little ones, weary,
No more can be merry;
The sun does descend,
And our sports have an end.
Round the laps of their mothers
Many sisters and brothers,
Like birds in their nest,
Are ready for rest,
And sport no more seen
On the darkening Green.

WILLIAM BLAKE

ERITH

There are men in the village of Erith
Whom nobody seeth or heareth,
    And there looms on the marge
    Of the river a barge
That nobody roweth or steereth.

THE FAIRIES' FAREWELL

Farewell, rewards and fairies,
    Good housewives now may say,
For now foul sluts in dairies
    Do fare as well as they;
And though they sweep their hearths no less
    Than maids were wont to do,
Yet who of late for cleanliness
    Finds sixpence in her shoe?

At morning and at evening both,
   You merry were and glad;
So little care of sleep and sloth
   These pretty ladies had;
When Tom came home from labour,
Or Ciss to milking rose,
   Then merrily went their tabor,
   And nimbly went their toes.

A tell-tale in their company
   They never could endure,
And whoso kept not secretly
   Their mirth was punished sure.
It was a just and Christian deed
   To pinch such black and blue;
Oh, how the Commonwealth doth need
   Such justices as you!

Witness those rings and roundelays
    Of theirs which yet remain,
Were footed in Queen Mary's days
    On many a grassy plain.
But since of late Elizabeth
    And later James came in,
They never danced on any heath
    As when the time had been.

By which we note the fairies
    Were of the old profession,
Their songs were Avé Maries,
    Their dances were procession.
But now alas, they all are dead
    Or gone beyond the seas,
Or further from religion fled,
    Or else they take their ease.

RICHARD CORBET

FAIRY THINGS

Grey lichens, mid thy hills of creeping thyme,
Grow like to fairy forests hung with rime;
And fairy money-pots are often found
That spring like little mushrooms out of ground,

Some shaped like cups and some in slender trim
Wineglasses like, that to the very rim
Are filled with little mystic shining seed;
We thought our fortunes promising indeed,
Expecting by and by ere night to find
Money ploughed up of more substantial kind.

Acres of little yellow weeds,
The wheat-field's constant blooms,
That ripen into prickly seeds
For fairy curry-combs,
To comb and clean the little things
That draw their nightly wain;
And so they scrub the beetle's wings
Till he can fly again.

And flannel for the beds of the queen
From the soft inside of the shell of the bean,
Where the gipsies down in the lonely dells
Had littered and left the plundered shells.

JOHN CLARE

THE FLINT

An emerald is as green as grass,
   A ruby red as blood,
A sapphire shines as blue as heaven;
   But a flint lies in the mud.
A diamond is a brilliant stone
   To catch the world's desire;
An opal holds a rainbow light,
   But a flint holds fire.

CHRISTINA ROSSETTI

FOUR CHILDREN

As I lay quietly in the grass,
   Half dreaming, half awake,
I saw four children barefoot pass
   Across the tufted brake:
The sky was glass, the pools were glass
   And not a leaf did shake.

The autumn berries clustered thick,
   Seldom I'd met with more:
I thought these children came to pick,
   As many picked before;
Each had a long and crooked stick,
   And crowns of ash they wore.

But not one berry did they take:
   Gliding, I watched them go
Hand in hand across the brake

With sallies to and fro,
So half asleep and half awake
    I guessed what now I know,

They were not children, live and rough,
    Nor phantoms of the dead,
But spirits woven of airy stuff,
    By wandering fancy led,
Creatures of silence, fair enough,
    No sooner seen than sped.

ROBERT GRAVES

FULL FATHOM FIVE

Full fathom five thy father lies;
Of his bones are coral made:
Those are pearls that were his eyes:
Nothing of him that doth fade,
But doth suffer a sea-change
Into something rich and strange.
Sea-nymphs hourly ring his knell:
    Ding-dong.
Hark! now I hear them,—ding-dong, bell.

WILLIAM SHAKESPEARE

GIBBERISH

Infirtaris,
Inoaknoneis.
Inmudeelsare,
Inclaynoneis.
Goateativy,
Mareeatoats.

GOD BE IN MY HEAD

God be in my head,
And in my understanding;

God be in mine eyes,
And in my looking;

God be in my mouth,
And in my speaking;

God be in my heart,
And in my thinking;

God be at mine end,
And at my departing.

GOD IS OUR REFUGE

God is our refuge and strength, a very present help in trouble.

Therefore will not we fear, though the earth be removed, and though the mountains be carried into the midst of the sea;

Though the waters thereof roar and be troubled, though the mountains shake with the swelling thereof.

from PSALM 46

GOLDEN SLUMBERS

Golden slumbers kiss your eyes,
Smiles awake you when you rise.
Sleep, pretty wantons, do not cry,
And I will sing a lullaby:
Rock them, rock them, lullaby.

Care is heavy, therefore sleep you;
You are care, and care must keep you.
Sleep, pretty wantons, do not cry,
And I will sing a lullaby:
Rock them, rock them, lullaby.

THOMAS DEKKER

THE GROVES OF BLARNEY

The groves of Blarney they are so charming,
    All by the purling of sweet silent streams;
Being banked with posies that spontaneous grow there,
    Planted in order by the sweet rock close.

'Tis there's the daisy and the sweet carnation,
   The blooming pink and the rose so fair;
The daffodowndilly, besides the lily,—
   Flowers that scent the sweet fragrant air.

RICHARD MILLIKIN

HARK, HARK! THE LARK

Hark, hark! the lark at Heaven's gate sings,
   And Phoebus gins arise,
His steeds to water at those springs
   On chaliced flowers that lies;
And winking mary-buds begin
   To ope their golden eyes;
With every thing that pretty is,
   My lady sweet, arise:
      Arise, arise!

WILLIAM SHAKESPEARE

HAUL AWAY, JOE

Way haul away! we'll haul away the bowline,
   Way haul away! we'll haul away Joe.
Way haul away! The packet is a-rollin'.
   Way haul away! we'll haul away Joe.

Geordie Charlton had a pig, and it was double-jointed.
   Way haul away! we'll haul away Joe.
He took it to the blacksmith's shop to get its trotters
   pointed.
   Way haul away! we'll haul away Joe.

King Louis was the king of France before the Revolution.
  Way haul away! we'll haul away Joe.
King Louis got his head cut off, and spoiled his Consti-
    tution.
  Way haul away! we'll haul away Joe.

Way haul away! we'll haul away together,
  Way haul away! we'll haul away Joe.
Way haul away! we'll haul for better weather,
  Way haul away! we'll haul away Joe.

HE THAT DWELLETH

He that dwelleth in the secret place of the most High shall
abide under the shadow of the Almighty.

I will say of the Lord, He is my refuge and my fortress:
my God; in him will I trust.

Surely he shall deliver thee from the snare of the fowler,
and from the noisome pestilence.

He shall cover thee with his feathers, and under his
wings shalt thou trust: his truth shall be thy shield and
buckler.

Thou shalt not be afraid for the terror by night; nor for the arrow that flieth by day;

Nor for the pestilence that walketh in darkness; nor for the destruction that wasteth at noonday.

from PSALM 91

THE HOLLY AND THE IVY

The holly and the ivy,
When they are both full grown,
Of all the trees that are in the wood,
The holly bears the crown:

> *The rising of the sun*
> *And the running of the deer,*
> *The playing of the merry organ,*
> *Sweet singing in the choir.*

The holly bears a blossom,
As white as the lily flower,
And Mary bore sweet Jesus Christ,
To be our sweet Saviour:

The holly bears a berry,
As red as any blood,
And Mary bore sweet Jesus Christ
To do poor sinners good:

The holly bears a prickle,
As sharp as any thorn,
And Mary bore sweet Jesus Christ
On Christmas day in the morn:

The holly bears a bark,
As bitter as any gall,
And Mary bore sweet Jesus Christ
For to redeem us all:

The holly and the ivy,
When they are both full grown,
Of all the trees that are in the wood,
The holly bears the crown.

HOW DOTH THE LITTLE BUSY BEE

How doth the little busy bee
   Improve each shining hour,
And gather honey all the day
   From every opening flower!

How skilfully she builds her cells!
   How neat she spreads the wax!
And labours hard to store it well
   With the sweet food she makes.

In works of labour or of skill,
   I would be busy too;
For Satan finds some mischief still
   For idle hands to do.

In books, or work, or healthful play,
   Let my first years be passed,
That I may give for every day
   Some good account at last.

ISAAC WATTS

HUNTING SONG

The dusky night rides down the sky
  And ushers in the morn;
The hounds all join in glorious cry,
  The Huntsman winds his horn:
    And a hunting we will go.

The wife around her husband throws
  Her arms, and begs him stay;
'My dear, it rains, and hails, and snows,
  You will not hunt to-day.'
    But a hunting we will go.

'A brushing fox in yonder wood,
  Secure to find we seek;
For why, I carried sound and good
  A cartload there last week.'
    And a hunting we will go.

Away he goes, he flies the rout,
    Their steeds all spur and switch;
Some are thrown in, and some thrown out,
    And some thrown in the ditch:
    But a hunting we will go.

At length his strength to faintness worn,
    Poor Reynard ceases flight;
Then hungry, homeward we return,
    To feast away the night:
    Then a drinking we will go.

HENRY FIELDING

HYND HORN

In Scotland there was a baby born,
    With a hey lilly loo and a how lo lan,
And his name it was called young Hynd Horn,
    And the birk and the broom blooms bonny.

He sent a letter to our King,
    With a hey lilly loo . . .
That he was in love with his daughter Jean,
    And the birk . . .

The King an angry man was he;
He sent young Hynd Horn to the sea.

He's given to her a silver wand,
With seven living laverocks* sitting thereon.

She's given to him a diamond ring,
With seven bright diamonds set therein.

* Seven larks carved or drawn on it in a life-like way.

'When this ring grows pale and wan,
You may know by it my love is gone.'

One day as he looked his ring upon,
He saw the diamonds pale and wan.

He left the sea and came to land,
And the first that he met was an old beggar-man.

'What news, what news?' said young Hynd Horn,
'No news, no news,' said the old beggar-man.

'No news,' said the beggar, 'no news at all,
But there is a wedding in the King's Hall.'

'Wilt thou lend me thy begging coat?
And I'll lend thee my scarlet cloak.

'Wilt thou lend me thy beggar's ring?
And I'll give thee my steed to ride upon.'

The old beggar-man was bound for to ride,
But young Hynd Horn was bound for the bride.

When he came to the King's gate,
He sought a drink for Hynd Horn's sake.

The bride came down with a glass of wine,
When he drank out the glass, and dropped in the ring.

'O, got ye this by sea or by land?
Or got thou it off a dead man's hand?'

'I got it not by sea, but I got it by land,
For I got it out of your fair hand.'

'O, I'll cast off my satin gown,
And follow you from town to town.

'I'll take the fine gold from my hair,
And follow you for ever more.'

The bridegroom wedded the bride that day,
With a hey lilly loo and a how lo lan,
But young Hynd Horn did steal her away,
And the birk and the broom blooms bonny.

I HAD FOUR BROTHERS

I had four brothers over the sea,
Perrie, Merrie, Dixi, Domine;
And they each sent a present unto me.
Petrum, Partrum, Paradisi, Tempore,
Perrie, Merrie, Dixi, Domine.

The first sent a goose without a bone,
Perrie, Merrie, Dixi, Domine;
The second sent a cherry without a stone,
Petrum, Partrum, Paradisi, Tempore,
Perrie, Merrie, Dixi, Domine.

The third sent a blanket without a thread,
Perrie, Merrie, Dixi, Domine;
The fourth sent a book that no man could read,
Petrum, Partrum, Paradisi, Tempore,
Perrie, Merrie, Dixi, Domine.

When the cherry's in the blossom, there is no stone,
Perrie, Merrie, Dixi, Domine;
When the goose is in the egg-shell, there is no bone,
Petrum, Partrum, Paradisi, Tempore,
Perrie, Merrie, Dixi, Domine.

When the wool's on the sheep's back, there is no thread,
Perrie, Merrie, Dixi, Domine;
When the book's in the press, no man can read,
Petrum, Partrum, Paradisi, Tempore,
Perrie, Merrie, Dixi, Domine.

IN SPRING-TIME

There's many a pool that holds a cloud
Deep down for miles to float along;
There's many a hedge that's white with may,
To bring the backward birds to song;

There's many a country lane that smells
Of beanfields, through the night and day;
Then why should I be here this hour,
In Spring-time, when the month is May?

There's nothing else but stone I see,
With but this ribbon of a sky;
And not a garden big enough
To share it with a butterfly.
Why do I walk these dull dark streets,
In gloom and silence all day long –
In Spring-time, when the blackbird's day
Is four and twenty hours of song?

W. H. DAVIES

JABBERWOCKY

'Twas brillig, and the slithy toves
    Did gyre and gimble in the wabe;
All mimsy were the borogoves,
    And the mome raths outgrabe.

'Beware the Jabberwock, my son!
    The jaws that bite, the claws that catch!
Beware the Jubjub bird, and shun
    The frumious Bandersnatch!'

He took his vorpal sword in hand:
    Long time the manxome foe he sought –
So rested he by the Tumtum tree,
    And stood awhile in thought.

And as in uffish thought he stood,
　The Jabberwock, with eyes of flame,
Came whiffling through the tulgey wood
　And burbled as it came!

One, two! One, two! And through and through
　The vorpal blade went snicker-snack!
He left it dead, and with its head
　He went galumphing back.

'And hast thou slain the Jabberwock?
　Come to my arms, my beamish boy!
O frabjous day! Callooh callay!'
　He chortled in his joy.

'Twas brillig, and the slithy toves
　Did gyre and gimble in the wabe;
All mimsy were the borogoves,
　And the mome raths outgrabe.

LEWIS CARROLL

JOHN TO JOAN

Quoth John to Joan: 'Wilt thou have me?
I prithee now, wilt? and I'll marry thee,
My cow, my calf, my house, my rents,
And all my lands and tenements:
　Oh, say, my Joan, will not that do?
　I cannot come every day to woo.

'I've corn and hay in the barn hard by,
And three fat hogs pent up in the sty,
I have a mare, and she is coal-black,
I ride on her tail to save her back.
    Then, say, my Joan, will not that do?
    I cannot come every day to woo.

'I have a cheese upon the shelf,
And I cannot eat it all myself:
I've three good marks that lie in a rag,
In a nook of the chimney, instead of a bag.
    Then, say, my Joan, will not that do?
    I cannot come every day to woo.

'To marry I would have thy consent,
But faith, I never could compliment;
I can say nought but "Hoy, gee ho!"
Words that belong to the cart and the plough.
    Then, say, my Joan, will not that do?
    I cannot come every day to woo.'

THE KEY OF THE KINGDOM

This is the key of the Kingdom:
In that Kingdom is a city;
In that city is a town;
In that town is a street;
In that street there winds a lane;
In that lane there is a yard;
In that yard there is a house;
In that house there waits a room;
In that room an empty bed,

And on that bed a basket —
A basket of sweet flowers
  Of flowers, of flowers;
  A basket of sweet flowers.

Flowers in a basket;
Basket on the bed;
Bed in the room;
Room in the house;
House in the yard;
Yard in the winding lane;
Lane in the street;
Street in the town;
Town in the city;
City in the Kingdom —
This is the key of the Kingdom.
  Of the Kingdom this is the key.

A LINNET IN HELL

A linnet who had lost her way
Sang on a blackened bough in Hell,
Till all the ghosts remembered well
The trees, the wind, the golden day.

At last they knew that they had died
When they heard music in that land,
And someone there stole forth a hand
To draw a brother to his side.

JAMES ELROY FLECKER

THE LITTLE BLACK BOY

My mother bore me in the southern wild,
   And I am black, but O my soul is white;
White as an angel is the English child,
   But I am black, as if bereaved of light.

My mother taught me underneath a tree,
   And, sitting down before the heat of day.
She took me on her lap and kisséd me,
   And, pointing to the east, began to say:

'Look on the rising sun, – there God does live,
   And gives his light, and gives his heat away;
And flowers and trees and beasts and men receive
   Comfort in morning, joy in the noonday.

'And we are put on earth a little space,
   That we may learn to bear the beams of love
And these black bodies and this sunburnt face
   Is but a cloud, and like a shady grove.

'For when our souls have learned the heat to bear,
   The cloud will vanish, we shall hear his voice,
Saying: "Come out from the grove, my love and care,
   And round my golden tent like lambs rejoice."'

Thus did my mother say, and kisséd me;
  And thus I say to little English boy:
When I from black, and he from white cloud free,
  And round the tent of God like lambs we joy,

I'll shade him from the heat, till he can bear
  To lean in joy upon our father's knee;
And then I'll stand and stroke his silver hair,
  And be like him, and he will then love me.

WILLIAM BLAKE

THE LORD IS MY SHEPHERD

The Lord is my shepherd; I shall not want.

He maketh me to lie down in green pastures:

He leadeth me beside the still waters.

He restoreth my soul:

He leadeth me in the paths of righteousness for his
  name's sake.

Yea, though I walk through the valley of the shadow
  of death,

I will fear no evil: for thou art with me; thy rod and
  thy staff they comfort me.

Thou preparest a table before me in the presence of
  mine enemies:

Thou anointest my head with oil, my cup runneth over.

Surely goodness and mercy shall follow me all the days
  of my life:

And I will dwell in the house of the Lord for ever.

PSALM 23

A MAN OF WORDS

A man of words and not of deeds
Is like a garden full of weeds;
And when the weeds begin to grow,
It's like a garden full of snow;
And when the snow begins to fall,
It's like a bird upon the wall;
And when the bird away does fly,
It's like an eagle in the sky;
And when the sky begins to roar,
It's like a lion at the door;
And when the door begins to crack,
It's like a stick across your back;
And when your back begins to smart,
It's like a penknife in your heart;
And when your heart begins to bleed,
You're dead, and dead, and dead indeed.

MIDNIGHT

(from *Christabel*)

'Tis the middle of night by the castle clock,
And the owls have awakened the crowing cock;
Tu-whit — Tu-whoo!
And hark, again! the crowing cock,
How drowsily it crew.

Sir Leoline, the baron rich,
Hath a toothless mastiff bitch;
From her kennel beneath the rock
She maketh answer to the clock,
Four for the quarters, and twelve for the hour;
Ever and aye, by shine and shower,
Sixteen short howls, not over loud:
Some say, she sees my lady's shroud.

Is the night chilly and dark?
The night is chilly, but not dark.
The thin grey cloud is spread on high,
It covers but not hides the sky.
The moon is behind, and at the full;
And yet she looks both small and dull.
The night is chill, the cloud is grey:
'Tis a month before the month of May,
And the Spring comes slowly up this way.

SAMUEL TAYLOR COLERIDGE

A MILKMAID

Two legs sat upon three legs,
  With four legs standing by;
Four were then drawn by ten:
Read my riddle ye can't,
  However much ye try.

THE MOATED GRANGE

(from *Mariana*)

With blackest moss the flower-plots
  Were thickly crusted, one and all;
The rusted nails fell from the knots
  That held the pear to the garden-wall.
The broken sheds looked sad and strange:
  Unlifted was the clinking latch;
  Weeded and worn the ancient thatch
Upon the lovely moated grange.

ALFRED TENNYSON

MY DANCING DAY

To-morrow shall be my dancing day;
  I would my true love did so chance
To see the legend of my play,
  To call my true love to my dance.
  Sing O my love, my love, my love —
  This have I done for my true love.

In a manger laid and wrapt I was,
    So very poor, this was my chance.
Betwixt an ox and a silly poor ass,
    To call my true love to my dance.
    Sing O my love, my love, my love –
    This have I done for my true love.

Into the desert I was led,
    Where I fasted without substance,
The devil bade me make stones my bread,
    To have me break my true love's dance.
    Sing O my love, my love, my love –
    This have I done for my true love.

For thirty pence Judas me sold
    His covetousness for to advance:
'Mark who I kiss, the same do hold,'
    The same is he shall lead the dance.
    Sing O my love, my love, my love –
    This have I done for my true love.

Then on the cross hangèd I was,
    Where a spear to my heart did glance;
There issued forth both water and blood,
    To call my true love to my dance.
    Sing O my love, my love, my love –
    This have I done for my true love.

Then down to Hell I took my way
    For my true love's deliverance,
And rose again on the third day
    Up to my true love and the dance.
    Sing O my love, my love, my love –
    This have I done for my true love.

MY GARDEN

The lilac in my garden comes to bloom
  The apple, plum and cherry wait their hour,
The honeysuckle climbs from pole to pole –
  And the rockery has a stone that's now a flower,
Jewelled by moss in every tiny hole!

Close to my lilac there's a small bird's nest
  Of quiet, young, half-sleeping birds: but when
I look, each little rascal – five I've reckoned –
  Opens a mouth so large and greedy then,
He swallows his own face in half a second!

W. H. DAVIES

NAILSWORTH HILL

The Moon, that peeped as she came up,
   Is clear on top, with all her light;
She rests her chin on Nailsworth Hill,
   And, where she looks, the World is white.

White with her light – or is it Frost,
   Or is it Snow her eyes have seen;
Or is it Cherry blossom there,
   Where no such trees have ever been?

W. H. DAVIES

A NEW YEAR CAROL

Here we bring new water
   From the well so clear,
For to worship God with
   This happy new year.

Sing levy dew, sing levy dew,
   The water and the wine;
The seven bright gold wires
   And the bugles that do shine.

Sing reign of Fair Maid,
   With gold upon her toe –
Open you the West Door,
   And turn the Old Year go.

Sing reign of Fair Maid,
    With gold upon her chin -
Open you the East Door,
    And let the New Year in.

Sing levy dew, sing levy dew,
    The water and the wine;
The seven bright gold wires
    And the bugles that do shine.

NIGHT

Swiftly walk over the western wave,
    Spirit of night!
Out of the misty eastern cave
Where, all the long and lone daylight,
Thou wovest dreams of joy and fear
Which make thee terrible and dear, —
    Swift be thy flight!
        from the poem by PERCY BYSSHE SHELLEY

NO JEWEL

No jewel from the rock
Is lovely as the dew,
Flashing with flamelike red
With sea-like blue.

No web the merchant weaves
Can rival hers —
The silk the spider spins
Across the furze.

WALTER DE LA MARE

O ME TATERS

O, me taters and me 'ot fried fish!
You can 'ave a little if you wish,
You can 'ave it on a plate or on a dish
　　Or in a little bit o' paper!

O WHAT IF THE FOWLER MY
BLACKBIRD HAS TAKEN?

O what if the fowler my blackbird has taken?
　　The roses of dawn blossom over the sea;
Awaken, my blackbird, awaken, awaken,
　　And sing to me out of my red fuchsia tree!

O what if the fowler my blackbird has taken?
   The sun lifts his head from the lap of the sea —
Awaken, my blackbird, awaken, awaken,
   And sing to me out of my red fuchsia tree!

O what if the fowler my blackbird has taken?
   The mountain grows white with the birds of the sea;
But down in my garden forsaken, forsaken,
   I'll weep all the day by my red fuchsia tree.

CHARLES DALMON

THE OAK-TREE

Says the old man to the oak-tree,
'Young and lusty was I, when I kenned* thee;
I was young and lusty, I was fair and clear,
Young and lusty was I mony a lang year;
But sair† failed am I, sair failed now,
Sair failed am I, sin I kenned thou.'

* Knew.   † Sore.

THE OLD FORESTER

I have been a forester long and many a day,
   My locks are hoar.
I shall hang up my horn by the greenwood spray;
   Forester will I be no more.

All the while that I may my bow bend
    Shall I wed no wife.
I shall build me a bower at the wood's end,
    There to lead my life.

OLD JOE BRADDLE-UM

Number One, Number One,
Now my song has just begun,
    With a rum-tum-taddle-um,
    Old Joe Braddle-um,
    Eh! what country folks we be.

Number Two, Number Two,
Some likes a boot but I likes a shoe,
    With a . . .

Number Three, Number Three,
Some likes coffee, but I likes tea,
    With a . . .

Number Four, Number Four,
Some likes a gate but I likes a door
    With a . . .

Number Five, Number Five,
Some likes 'em dead but I likes 'em live,
    With a . . .

Number Six, Number Six,
Some likes stones, but I likes sticks,
  With a . . .

Number Seven, Number Seven
Is just the same as Number Eleven,
  With a . . .

Number Eight, Number Eight,
Some likes a door, but I likes a gate,
  With a . . .

Number Nine, Number Nine,
Some likes ale but I likes wine,
  With a . . .

Number Ten, Number Ten,
Some likes a cock but I likes a hen,
  With a . . .

Number Eleven, Number Eleven
Is just the same as Number Seven,
  With a . . .

Number Twelve, Number Twelve,
If you want any more you can say it yourself,
  With a . . .

THE OLD PERSON OF CASSEL

There was an old person of Cassel,
Whose nose finished off in a tassel;
    But they called out, 'Oh well!
    Don't it look like a bell!'
Which perplexed that old person of Cassel.

EDWARD LEAR

THE OLD PERSON OF DEAN

There was an old person of Dean
Who dined on one pea, and one bean;
    For he said, 'More than that,
    Would make me too fat,'
That cautious old person of Dean.

EDWARD LEAR

THE OLD PERSON OF JODD

There was an old person of Jodd,
Whose ways were perplexing and odd;
    She purchased a whistle,
    And sat on a thistle,
And squeaked to the people of Jodd.

EDWARD LEAR

THE RAVEN

Underneath an old oak tree
There was of swine a huge company,
That grunted as they crunched the mast:
For that was ripe, and fell full fast.
Then they trotted away, for the wind grew high:
One acorn they left, and no more might you spy.
Next came a Raven, that liked not such folly:
He belonged, they did say, to the witch Melancholy!
Blacker was he than blackest jet,
Flew low in the rain, and his feathers not wet.
He picked up the acorn and buried it straight
By the side of a river both deep and great.
   Where then did the Raven go?
   He went high and low,
Over hill, over dale, did the black Raven go.
   Many Autumns, many Springs,
   Travelled he with wandering wings:
   Many Summers, many Winters –
   I can't tell half his adventures.

At length he came back, and with him a She,
And the acorn was grown to a tall oak tree.
They built them a nest in the topmost bough,
And young ones they had, and were happy enow.
But soon came a Woodman in leathern guise,
His brow, like a pent-house, hung over his eyes.
He'd an axe in his hand, not a word he spoke,
But with many a hem! and a sturdy stroke,
At length he brought down the poor Raven's own oak.
His young ones were killed; for they could not depart,
And their mother did die of a broken heart.

The boughs from the trunk the Woodman did sever;
And they floated it down on the course of the river.
They sawed it in planks, and its bark they did strip
And with this tree and others they made a good ship.
The ship it was launched; but in sight of the land
Such a storm there did rise as no ship could withstand.
It bulged on a rock, and the waves rushed in fast:
Round and round flew the Raven, and cawed to the blast.
He heard the last shriek of the perishing souls —
See! see! o'er the topmast the mad water rolls!

Right glad was the Raven, and off he went fleet,
And Death riding home on a cloud he did meet,
And he thanked him again and again for this treat:
They had taken his all, and REVENGE IT WAS
SWEET!

SAMUEL TAYLOR COLERIDGE

REEDS OF INNOCENCE

Piping down the valleys wild,
    Piping songs of pleasant glee,
On a cloud I saw a child,
    And he laughing said to me:

'Pipe a song about a Lamb!'
    So I piped with merry cheer.
'Piper, pipe that song again';
    So I piped: he wept to hear.

'Drop thy pipe, thy happy pipe;
    Sing thy songs of happy cheer':
So I sang the same again,
    While he wept with joy to hear.

'Piper, sit thee down and write
    In a book, that all may read.'
So he vanished from my sight,
    And I plucked a hollow reed,

And I made a rural pen,
    And I stained the water clear,
And I wrote my happy songs
    Every child may joy to hear.

WILLIAM BLAKE

THE RIDDLING KNIGHT

A knight came riding from the East,
    Jennifer, gentle and rosemarie,
Who had been wooing at many a place,
    As the dove flies over the mulberry tree.

He came and knocked at the lady's gate,
    Jennifer, gentle . . .
One evening when it was growing late,
    As the dove . . .

The eldest sister let him in,
And pinned the door with a silver pin.

The second sister, she made his bed
And laid soft pillows under his head.

The youngest sister was bold and bright
And she would wed with this unco Knight.

'If you will answer me questions three,
This very day will I marry thee.

'O, what is louder nor a horn?
And what is sharper nor a thorn?

'What is heavier nor the lead?
And what is better nor the bread?

'O, what is higher nor the tree?
And what is deeper nor the sea?'

'O, shame is louder nor a horn,
And hunger is sharper nor a thorn.

'And sin is heavier nor the lead,
And the blessing's better nor the bread.

'O, Heaven is higher nor the tree,
And love is deeper nor the sea.'

'O, you have answered my questions three,
    Jennifer, gentle and rosemarie,
And so, fair maid, I'll marry with thee,
    As the dove flies over the mulberry tree.'

ROBIN GOODFELLOW

From Oberon in Fairyland
  The king of ghosts and shadows there
Mad Robin I, at his command,
  Am sent to view the night-sports here
    What revel rout
    Is kept about
  In every corner where I go.
    I will o'er sea
    And merry be,
  And make good sport with ho, ho, ho!

More swift than lightning can I fly
  About this airy welkin soon,
And in a minute's space descry
  Each thing that's done below the moon.
    There's not a hag
    Or ghost shall wag,
  Or cry 'Ware goblins' where I go;
    But Robin I
    Their feats will spy
  And send them home with ho, ho, ho!

Whene'er such wanderers I meet,
  As from their night-sports they trudge home,
With counterfeiting voice I greet
  And call them on with me to roam
    Through woods, through lakes,
    Through bogs, through brakes;
  Or else unseen with them I go,
    All in the nick
    To play some trick
  And frolic it with ho, ho, ho!

Sometimes I meet them like a man;
   Sometimes an ox, sometimes a hound;
And to a horse I turn me can;
   To trip and trot about them round.
     But if to ride
     My back they stride,
   More swift than wind away I go,
     O'er hedge and lands,
     Through pools and ponds,
   I whirry, laughing ho, ho, ho!

Yet now and then, the maids to please,
   At midnight I card up their wool;
And when they sleep and take their ease,
   With wheel to thread their flax I pull.
     I grind at mill
     Their malt up still;
   I dress their hemp, I spin their tow,
     If any wake,
     And would me take,
   I wend me, laughing ho, ho, ho!

When men do traps and engines set
   In loopholes where the vermin creep,
Who from their folds and houses get
   Their ducks and geese, their lambs and sheep,
     I spy the gin,*
     I enter in
   And seem a vermin taken so;
     But when they there
     Approach me near,
   I leap out, laughing ho, ho, ho!

* Trap

From hag-bred Merlin's time have I
   Thus nightly revelled to and fro;
And from my pranks men call me by
   The name of Robin Goodfellow,
     Friends, ghosts, and sprites
     Who haunt the nights,
   The hags and goblins do we know,
     And beldames old
     My feats have told,
So Valé, valé!* ho, ho, ho!

BEN JONSON

* Farewell.

ROBIN HOOD AND
ALAN A DALE

Come listen to me, you gallants so free,
   All you that love mirth for to hear,
And I will tell you of a bold outláw,
   That lived in Nottinghamshire.

As Robin Hood in the forest stood,
   All under the green-wood tree,
There was he ware of a brave young man,
   As fine as fine might be.

The youngster was clothed in scarlet red,
   In scarlet fine and gay,
And he did frisk it over the plain,
   And chanted a roundelay.

As Robin Hood next morning stood,
  Amongst the leaves so gay,
There did he espy the same young man
  Come drooping along the way.

The scarlet he wore the day before,
  It was clean cast away;
And every step he fetched a sigh,
  'Alack and a well a day!'

Then steppéd forth brave Little John,
  And Much the miller's son,
Which made the young man bend his bow,
  When as he saw them come.

'Stand off, stand off!' the young man said,
  'What is your will with me?' –
'You must come before our master straight,
  Under yon green-wood tree.'

And when he came bold Robin before,
  Robin asked him courteously,
'O hast thou any money to spare,
  For my merry men and me?'

'I have no money,' the young man said,
　'But five shillings and a ring;
And that I have kept this seven long years,
　To have it at my wedding.

'Yesterday I should have married a maid,
　But she is now from me ta'en,
And chosen to be an old knight's delight,
　Whereby my poor heart is slain.'

'What is thy name?' then said Robin Hood,
　'Come tell me, without any fail.' —
'By the faith of my body,' then said the young man,
　'My name it is Alan a Dale.'

'What wilt thou give me,' said Robin Hood,
　'In ready gold or fee,
To help thee to thy true-love again,
　And deliver her unto thee?'

'I have no money,' then quoth the young man,
　'No ready gold nor fee,
But I will swear upon a book
　Thy true servant for to be.' —

'But how many miles to thy true-love?
    Come tell me without any guile.' —
'By the faith of my body,' then said the young man,
    'It is but five little mile.'

Then Robin he hasted over the plain,
    He did neither stint nor lin,*
Until he came unto the church
    Where Alan should keep his wedding.

'What dost thou do here?' the Bishop he said,
    'I prithee now tell to me':
'I am a bold harper,' quoth Robin Hood,
    'And the best in the north country.'

'O welcome, O welcome!' the Bishop he said,
    'That music best pleaseth me.' —
'You shall have no music,' quoth Robin Hood,
    'Till the bride and the bridegroom I see.'

With that came in a wealthy knight,
    Which was both grave and old,
And after him a finikin† lass,
    Did shine like glistering gold.

'This is no fit match,' quoth bold Robin Hood,
    'That you do seem to make here;
For since we are come unto the church,
    The bride she shall choose her own dear.'

* Stop.   † Dainty.

240

Then Robin Hood put his horn to his mouth,
  And blew blasts two or three;
When four and twenty bowmen bold
  Come leaping over the lee.

And when they came into the churchyard,
  Marching all on a row,
The first man was Alan a Dale,
  To give bold Robin his bow.

'This is thy true-love,' Robin he said,
  'Young Alan, as I hear say;
And you shall be married at this same time,
  Before we depart away.'

'That shall not be,' the Bishop he said,
  'For thy word it shall not stand;
They shall be three times asked in the church,
  As the law is of our land.'

Robin Hood pull'd off the Bishop's coat,
  And put it upon Little John;
'By the faith of my body,' then Robin said,
  'This cloth doth make thee a man.'

When Little John went into the choir,
  The people began for to laugh;
He asked them seven times in the church,
  Lest three should not be enough.

'Who gives me this maid?' then said Little John;
  Quoth Robin, 'That do I!
And he that doth take her from Alan a Dale
  Full dearly he shall her buy.'

And thus having ended this merry wedding,
   The bride looked as fresh as a queen,
And so they returned to the merry green-wood,
   Amongst the leaves so green.

A ROBIN'S EPITAPH

Tread lightly here, for here, 'tis said,
When piping winds are hushed around,
A small note wakes from underground,
Where now his tiny bones are laid.

No more in lone or leafless groves,
With ruffled wing and faded breast,
His friendless, homeless spirit roves;
Gone to the world where birds are blessed.

Where never cat glides o'er the green,
Or schoolboy's giant form is seen;
But love and joy and smiling Spring
Inspire their little souls to sing.

SAMUEL ROGERS

ROCK, BALL, FIDDLE

He that lies at the stock
   Shall have the gold rock;
He that lies at the wall
   Shall have the gold ball;
He that lies in the middle
   Shall have the gold fiddle.

SHEEP

When I was once in Baltimore,
   A man came up to me and cried,
'Come, I have eighteen hundred sheep
   And we sail on Tuesday's tide.'

'If you will sail with me, young man,
   I'll pay you fifty shillings down;
These eighteen hundred sheep I take
   From Baltimore to Glasgow town.'

He paid me fifty shillings down,
   I sailed with eighteen hundred sheep;
We soon had cleared the harbour's mouth,
   We soon were in the salt sea deep.

The first night we were out at sea
   Those sheep were quiet in their mind;
The second night they cried with fear —
   They smelt no pastures in the wind.

They sniffed, poor things, for their green fields,
   They cried so loud I could not sleep:
For fifty thousand shillings down
   I would not sail again with sheep.

W. H. DAVIES

SILVER

Slowly, silently, now the moon
Walks the night in her silver shoon;
This way, and that, she peers, and sees
Silver fruit upon silver trees;
One by one the casements catch
Her beams beneath the silvery thatch;
Couched in his kennel like a log,
With paws of silver sleeps the dog;
From their shadowy cote the white breasts peep
Of doves in a silver-feathered sleep;
The harvest mouse goes scampering by,
With silver claws, and silver eye;
And moveless fish in the water gleam,
By silver reeds in a silver stream.

WALTER DE LA MARE

SIR EGLAMOUR

Sir Eglamour, that worthy knight,
He took up his sword and he went for to fight:
And as he rode over hill and dale,
All arméd with a coat of mail,
There starts a huge dragon out of her den,
Which had killed I know not how many men.
   Fa, la, lanky-down-dilly.

This dragon had a plaguey hard hide,
Which could the strongest steel abide;
No sword will enter her with cuts,
Which vexed the knight unto his guts;

But when she saw Sir Eglamour —
If you'd but heard how the dragon did **roar**.
   Fa, la, lanky-down-dilly.

To it they go, and fiercely fight
The whole of a day from morn till night.
With choler great the knight did burn,
He watched the dragon a good turn,
And as a-yawning she did fall,
He thrust his sword in, hilts and all.
   Fa, la, lanky-down-dilly.

The sword it was a right good blade,
As ever Turk or Spaniard made;
The dragon laid her down and roared.
The knight was sorry for his sword,

And, riding thence, said, 'I forsake it,
He that will fetch it, let him take it!'
   Fa, la, lanky-down-dilly.

When all was done, to the ale-house he went,
And presently all of his tuppence was spent.
He was so hot with fighting the dragon
That nought could quench his thirst but a flagon.
So here's to the knight, and as many more
Who are all as brave as Sir Eglamour!
   Fa, la, lanky-down-dilly.

SAMUEL ROWLANDS

SIR JOHN BARLEYCORN

There came three men from out the West
Their victory to try;
And they have ta'en a solemn oath,
Poor Barleycorn should die.

They took a plough and ploughed him in,
Clods harrowed on his head;
And then they took a solemn oath
John Barleycorn was dead.

There he lay sleeping in the ground
Till rain did on him fall;
Then Barleycorn sprung up his head,
And so amazed them all.

There he remained till Midsummer
And look'd both pale and wan;
Then Barleycorn he got a beard
And so became a man.

Then they sent men with scythes so sharp
To cut him off at knee;
And then poor Johnny Barleycorn
They served most barbarouslie.

Then they sent men with pitchforks strong
To pierce him through the heart;
And like a doleful Tragedy
They bound him in a cart.

And then they brought him to a barn
A prisoner to endure;
And so they fetched him out again,
And laid him on the floor.

Then they set men with holly clubs,
To beat the flesh from th' bones;
But the miller served him worse than that
He ground him 'twixt two stones.

O! Barleycorn is the choicest grain
That e'er was sown on land.
It will do more than any grain,
By the turning of your hand.

It will make a boy into a man,
A man into an ass;
To silver it will change your gold,
Your silver into brass.

It will make the huntsman hunt the fox,
That never wound a horn;
It will bring the tinker to the stocks
That people may him scorn.

O! Barleycorn is the choicest grain,
That e'er was sown on land.
And it will cause a man to drink
Till he neither can go nor stand.

SISTER, AWAKE!

Sister, awake! close not your eyes!
   The day her light discloses,
And the bright morning doth arise
   Out of her bed of roses.

See the clear sun, the world's bright eye,
   In at our window peeping;
Lo, how he blusheth to espy
   Us idle wenches sleeping!

Therefore awake! make haste, I say,
　　And let us, without staying,
All in our gowns of green so gay
　　Into the Park a-maying!

THE SLAIN KNIGHT

My love he built me a bonny bower,
And clad it all with lily-flower;
A braver bower ye ne'er did see
Than my true love he built for me.

There came a man by middle day,
He spied his sport and went away;
And brought the king that very night,
Who broke my bower and slew my knight.

He slew my knight to me so dear;
He slew my knight and took his gear;
My servants all for life did flee,
And left me in extremity.

I sewed his sheet, making my moan;
I watched the corpse, myself alone;
I watched his body night and day;
No living creature came that way.

I took his body on my back,
Sometimes I walked and sometimes sat;
I digged a grave and laid him in,
And covered him with sods so green.

But think ye not my heart was sore,
When I laid the mould on his yellow hair?
O think not ye my heart was woe,
When I turned about, away to go?

No living man I'll love again,
Since that my lovely knight is slain;
With one lock of his yellow hair,
I'll chain my heart for ever more.

SNOW AND SUN

White bird, featherless,
  Flew from Paradise,
Pitched on the castle wall;
  Along came Lord Landless,
  Took it up handless,
And rode away horseless to the King's white hall.

SO SHE WENT INTO
THE GARDEN

So she went into the garden to cut a cabbage to make an
    apple-pie.
Just then a great she-bear, coming down the street,
    poked its nose into the shop-window.
'What no soap?'
So he died, and she very imprudently married the barber.
And there were present at the wedding the Joblillies, and
    the Piccannies, and the Garyulies —

And the Great Pan Jandrum himself, with the little
  button on top!
So they fell to playing Catch-as-catch-can, till the
  gunpowder ran out at the heels of their boots.

SAMUEL FOOTE

SPRING

Spring, the sweet Spring, is the year's pleasant king
Then blooms each thing; then maids dance in a ring
Cold doth not sting; the pretty birds do sing,
  Cuckoo, jug-jug, pu-we, to-witta-woo!

The palm and may make country houses gay;
Lambs frisk and play: the shepherds pipe all day;
And we hear aye birds tune this merry lay,
  Cuckoo, jug-jug, pu-we, to-witta-woo!

The fields breathe sweet; the daisies kiss our feet;
Young lovers meet; old wives a-sunning sit;
In every street these tunes our ears do greet,
  Cuckoo, jug-jug, pu-we, to-witta-woo!
    Spring, the sweet Spring!

THOMAS NASHE

STAND! WHO GOES THERE

Watch: Stand! who goes there?
            We charge you appear
            'Fore our constable here,
            In the name of the Man in the Moon.

251

To us billmen relate,
Why you stagger so late,
And how you come drunk so soon.

Pages: What are ye, scabs?

Watch: The watch:
This the constable.

Pages: A patch!

Constable: Knock 'em down unless they all stand;
If any run away,
'Tis the old watchman's play,
To reach him a bill of his hand.

Pages: O gentlemen, hold,
Your gowns freeze with cold,
And your rotten teeth dance in your head.
Wine nothing shall cost ye;
Nor huge fires to roast ye;
Then soberly let us be led.

Constable: Come, my brown bills, we'll roar,
Bounce loud at tavern door.

All: And i' th' morning steal all to bed.

JOHN LYLY

STORMALONG

Old Stormy he is dead and gone,
To my way, Stormalong!
Old Stormy he is dead and gone,
Aye, aye, aye, Mister Stormalong.

Old Stormy's dead, that good old man,
To my way, Stormalong!
Old Stormy's dead, that good old man,
Aye, aye, aye, Mister Stormalong.

I carried him away to Mobile Bay,
To my way, Stormalong!
I carried him away to Mobile Bay,
Aye, aye, aye, Mister Stormalong.

I dug his grave with a silver spade,
To my way, Stormalong!
I dug his grave with a silver spade,
Aye, aye, aye, Mister Stormalong.

I lowered him down with a golden chain,
To my way, Stormalong!
I lowered him down with a golden chain,
Aye, aye, aye, Mister Stormalong.

I dug his grave full wide and deep,
To my way, Stormalong!
And there Old Stormy lies asleep,
Aye, aye, aye, Mister Stormalong.

I wish I was Old Stormy's son,
   To my way, Stormalong!
I'd build a ship a thousand ton,
   Aye, aye, aye, Mister Stormalong.

Old Stormy he is dead and gone.
   To my way, Stormalong!
Old Stormy he is dead and gone,
   Aye, aye, aye, Mister Stormalong.

STRAWBERRY FAIR

As I was going to Strawberry Fair,
   Singing, singing, buttercups and daisies,
I met a maiden taking her ware,
   Fol-de-dee!
Her eyes were blue and golden her hair,
As she went on to Strawberry Fair,
   Ri-fol, ri-fol, tol-de-riddle-i-do,
   Ri-fol, ri-fol, tol-de-riddle-dee.

'Kind sir, pray pick of my basket!' she said,
   Singing, singing, buttercups and daisies,
'My cherries ripe or my roses red,
   Fol-de dee!
My strawberries sweet I can of them spare,
As I go on to Strawberry Fair.'
   Ri-fol, ri-fol . . .

Your cherries soon will be wasted away,
   Singing, singing, buttercups and daisies,
Your roses wither and never stay,
   Fol-de-dee!

'Tis not to seek such perishing ware,
That I am tramping to Strawberry Fair.
  Ri-fol, ri-fol . . .

I want to purchase a generous heart,
 Singing, singing, buttercups and daisies,
A tongue that is neither nimble nor tart,
  Fol-de-dee!
An honest mind—but such trifles are rare,
I doubt if they're found at Strawberry Fair.
  Ri-fol, ri-fol . . .

The price I offer, my sweet pretty maid,
 Singing, singing, buttercups and daisies,
A ring of gold on your finger displayed;
  Fol-de-dee!
So come, make over to me your ware
In church to-day at Strawberry Fair.
  Ri-fol, ri-fol . . .

SWEET SUFFOLK OWL

Sweet Suffolk owl, so trimly dight*
With feathers like a lady bright,
Thou sing'st alone, sitting by night,
  Tu-whit, tu-whoo!

Thy note, that forth so freely rolls,
With shrill command the mouse controls,
And sings a dirge for dying souls,
  Tu-whit, tu-whoo!

        THOMAS VAUTOR

  * Dressed.

255

SYLVIA

Who is Sylvia? what is she,
    That all our swains commend her?
Holy, fair, and wise is she;
    The heaven such grace did lend her,
That she might admirèd be.

Is she kind as she is fair?
    For beauty lives with kindness.
Love doth to her eyes repair,
    To help him of his blindness;
And, being helped, inhabits there.

Then to Sylvia let us sing,
    That Sylvia is excelling;
She excels each mortal thing,
    Upon the dull earth dwelling:
To her let us garlands bring.

WILLIAM SHAKESPEARE

THREE JOVIAL WELSHMEN

There were three jovial Welshmen,
    As I have heard them say,
And they would go a-hunting
    Upon St David's day.

All the day they hunted,
    And nothing could they find
But a ship a-sailing,
    A-sailing with the wind.

One said it was a ship;
  The other he said nay;
The third said it was a house
  With the chimney blown away.

And all the night they hunted,
  And nothing could they find
But the moon a-gliding,
  A-gliding with the wind.

One said it was the moon;
  The other he said nay;
The third said it was a cheese
  And half of it cut away.

And all the day they hunted,
  And nothing could they find
But a hedgehog in a bramble-bush
  And that they left behind.

The first said it was a hedgehog;
  The second he said nay;
The third it was a pin cushion,
  And the pins stuck in wrong way.

And all the night they hunted,
  And nothing could they find
But a hare in a turnip field,
  And that they left behind.

The first said it was a hare;
   The second he said nay;
The third said it was a calf
   And the cow had run away.

And all the day they hunted,
   And nothing could they find
But an owl in a holly-tree,
   And that they left behind.

One said it was an owl;
   The other he said nay;
The third it was an old man,
   And his beard a-growing grey.

There were three jovial Welshmen,
   As I have heard them say.
And they would go a-hunting
   Upon St David's day.

TURTLE SOUP

Beautiful soup, so rich and green,
Waiting in a hot tureen!
Who for such dainties would not stoop?
Soup of the evening, beautiful soup!
Soup of the evening, beautiful soup!
    Beau – ootiful soo – oop!
    Beau – ootiful soo – oop!
Soo – oop of the e – e – evening,
    Beautiful, beautiful soup!

Beautiful soup! Who cares for fish,
Game, or any other dish?
Who would not give all else for two p
ennyworth only of beautiful soup?
Pennyworth only of beautiful soup?
    Beau – ootiful soo – oop!
    Beau – ootiful soo – oop!
Soo – oop of the e – e – evening,
    Beautiful, beauti – FUL SOUP!

LEWIS CARROLL

THE TWO MAGICIANS

O She looked out of the window,
   As white as any milk;
But He looked into the window,
   As black as any silk.
Chorus. Hallo, hallo, hallo, hallo, you coal-black
      smith!
    O what is your silly song?
   You never shall change my maiden name
    That I have kept so long;
   I'd rather die a maid, yes, but then she said,
    And be buried all in my grave,
   Than I'd have such a nasty, husky, dusky,
    musty, fusky,
    Coal-black smith

                A maiden I will die.

Then She became a duck,
   A duck all on the stream;
And he became a water-dog,
   And fetched her back again.
Chorus. Hallo, hallo . . .

Then She became a hare,
   A hare all on the plain;
And he became a greyhound dog,
   And fetched her back again.
Chorus. Hallo, hallo . . .

Then She became a fly,
   A fly all in the air;
And He became a spider,
   And fetched her to his lair.
Chorus. Hallo, hallo . . .

UNDER THE GREENWOOD TREE

Under the greenwood tree
Who loves to lie with me,
And tune his merry note
Unto the sweet bird's throat,
Come hither, come hither, come hither;
Here shall he see
No enemy
But winter and rough weather.

Who doth ambition shun,
And loves to live i' the sun,
Seeking the food he eats,
And pleased with what he gets,
Come hither, come hither, come hither;
Here shall he see
No enemy
But winter and rough weather.

WILLIAM SHAKESPEARE

THE USEFUL PLOUGH

A country life is sweet!
In moderate cold and heat,
To walk in the air, how pleasant and fair,
In every field of wheat,
The fairest of flowers adorning the bowers,
And every meadow's brow;
So that I say, no courtier may
Compare with them who clothe in grey,
And follow the useful plough.

They rise with morning lark,
And labour till almost dark;
　Then folding their sheep, they hasten to sleep;
While every pleasant park
　Next morning is ringing with birds that are
　　singing,
On each green, tender bough,
　With what content and merriment,
Their days are spent whose minds are bent
　To follow the useful plough!

VENETA

Wind and waters ring the bells
　That rang for them of high degree,
Trumpets are the sounding shells
　In the city under the sea.

Where a queen was wont to hide
　Her outwearied majesty,
Swim the fishes open-eyed
　In the city under the sea.

Many a street lies broad and fair,
　Many a palace fair and free,
Neither a man nor woman there,
　In the city under the sea.

MARY COLERIDGE

THE WANDERING SPECTRE

Woe's me, woe's me,
The acorn's not yet fallen from the tree
That's to grow the wood,
That's to make the cradle,
That's to rock the bairn,
That's to grow a man,
That's to lay me.

WE BE THE KING'S MEN

We be the King's men, hale and hearty,
Marching to meet one Buonaparty;
If he won't sail, lest the wind should blow,
We shall have marched for nothing, O!
    Right fol-lol!

We be the King's men, hale and hearty,
Marching to meet one Buonaparty;
If he be sea-sick, says 'No, no!'
We shall have marched for nothing, O!
    Right fol-lol!

We be the King's men, hale and hearty,
Marching to meet one Buonaparty;
Never mind mates; we'll be merry, though
We may have marched for nothing, O!
    Right fol-lol!

THOMAS HARDY

WHERE THE BEE SUCKS

Where the bee sucks, there suck I,
In a cowslip's bell I lie,
There I couch when owls do cry;
On the bat's back I do fly
After summer merrily.
Merrily, merrily, shall I live now
Under the blossom that hangs on the bough.

WILLIAM SHAKESPEARE

THE WHITETHORN-TREE

The fair, fair maid, on the first of May,
That goes to the fields at break of day,
And washes in dew by the whitethorn-tree,
Will ever blithe and bonny be.

WHO WOULD TRUE VALOUR SEE

(from *The Pilgrim's Progress*)

Who would true valour see,
    Let him come hither;
One here will constant be,
    Come wind, come weather.
There's no discouragement
Shall make him once relent
His first avow'd intent
    To be a pilgrim.

Whoso beset him round
    With dismal stories,
Do but themselves confound,
    His strength the more is.
No lion can him fright,
He'll with a giant fight,
But he will have a right
    To be a pilgrim.

Hobgoblin nor foul fiend
    Can daunt his spirit;
He knows he at the end
    Shall life inherit.
Then fancies flee away!
He'll fear not what men say;
He'll labour night and day
    To be a pilgrim.

JOHN BUNYAN

WIDDECOMBE FAIR

'Tom Pearse, Tom Pearse, lend me your grey mare,
All along, down along, out along lee;
For I want for to go to Widdecombe Fair,
Wi' Bill Brewer, Jan Stewer, Peter Gurney, Peter Davy,
    Dan'l Whiddon, Harry Hawke,
Old Uncle Tom Cobleigh and all,'
Old Uncle Tom Cobleigh and all.

'And when shall I see again my grey mare?'
All along, . . .
'By Friday soon or Saturday noon,'
Wi' Bill Brewer, . . .

Then Friday came, and Saturday noon,
All along, . . .
But Tom Pearse's old mare hath not trotted home,
Wi' Bill Brewer, . . .

So Tom Pearse he got up to the top o' the hill,
All along, . . .
And he see'd his old mare down a-making her will
Wi' Bill Brewer, . . .

So Tom Pearse's old mare, her took sick and her died,
All along, . . .
And Tom he sat down on a stone, and he cried
Wi' Bill Brewer, . . .

And now that Tom Pearse's old grey mare is dead
All along, . . .
They all did agree that she should be buried
Wi' Bill Brewer, . . .

But this isn't the end o' this shocking affair,
All along, . . .
Nor, though they be dead, of the horrid career
Of Bill Brewer, . . .

When the wind whistles cold on the moor of a night,
All along, . . .
Tom Pearse's old mare doth appear gashly white,
Wi' Bill Brewer, . . .

And all the night long be heard skirling and groans
All along, down along, out along lee;
From Tom Pearse's old mare in her rattling bones,
And from Bill Brewer, Jan Stewer, Peter Gurney,
    Peter Davy, Dan'l Whiddon, Harry Hawke,
Old Uncle Tom Cobleigh and all,
Old Uncle Tom Cobleigh and all.

A WIDOW BIRD

A widow bird sate mourning for her love
    Upon a wintry bough;
The frozen wind crept on above,
    The freezing stream below.

There was no leaf upon the forest bare,
    No flower upon the ground,
And little motion in the air
    Except the mill-wheel's sound.

PERCY BYSSHE SHELLEY

WILL YOU WALK
A LITTLE FASTER?

'Will you walk a little faster?' said a whiting to a snail.
'There's a porpoise close behind us, and he's treading
    on my tail.
See how eagerly the lobsters and the turtles all advance!
They are waiting on the shingle – will you come and join
    the dance?
Will you, won't you, will you, won't you, will you join the
    dance?
Will you, won't you, will you, won't you, won't you join
    the dance?

'You can really have no notion how delightful it will be,
When they take us up and throw us, with the lobsters
    out to sea!'
But the snail replied 'Too far, too far!' and gave a look
    askance –

Said he thanked the whiting kindly, but he would not
   join the dance.
Would not, could not, would not, could not, would not
   join the dance.
Would not, could not, would not, could not, could not
   join the dance.

'What matters it how far we go?' his scaly friend replied.
'There is another shore, you know, upon the other side.
The further off from England the nearer is to France –
Then turn not pale, beloved snail, but come and join the
   dance.
Will you, won't you, will you, won't you, will you join
   the dance?
Will you, won't you, will you, won't you, won't you join
   the dance?'

LEWIS CARROLL

WINTER

The frost is here,
The fuel is dear,
And woods are sear,
And fires burn clear,
And frost is here
And has bitten the heel of the going year.

Bite, frost, bite!
You roll up away from the light,
The blue wood-louse and the plump dormouse,
And the bees are stilled and the flies are killed,
And you bite far into the heart of the house,
But not into mine.

Bite, frost, bite!
The woods are all the searer,
The fuel is all the dearer,
The fires are all the clearer,
My spring is all the nearer,
You have bitten into the heart of the earth,
But not into mine.

ALFRED TENNYSON

THE WITCH
STEPMOTHER

'I was but seven year old
   When my mother she did die;
My father married the very worst woman
   The world did ever see.

For she has made me the loathly worm*
   That lies at the foot of the tree,
And my sister Maisry she's made
   The mackerel of the sea.

* Serpent.

And every Saturday at noon
   The mackerel comes to me,
And she takes my loathly head
   And lays it on her knee,
She combs it with a silver comb,
   And washes it in the sea.

Seven knights have I slain,
   Since I lay at the foot of the tree,
And were ye not my own father,
   The eighth one ye should be.'

The father sent for his lady,
   As fast as send could he:
'Where is my son that ye sent from me,
   And my daughter Lady Maisry?'

'Your son is at our king's court,
   Serving for meat and fee;
And your daughter's at our queen's court,
   A waiting-woman is she.'

'Ye lie, ye ill woman,
   So loud I hear ye lie:
My son's the loathly worm,
   That lies at the foot of the tree,
And my daughter Lady Maisry
   Is the mackerel of the sea!'

She has taken a silver wand,
   And given him strokes three,
And he's started up the bravest knight
   That ever your eyes did see.

She has taken a small horn,
    And loud and shrill blew she,
And all the fish came unto her
    But the proud mackerel of the sea:
'Ye shaped me once an unseemly shape
    Ye shall never more shape me.'

He has sent to the wood
    For whins and for hawthorn,
And he has taken that gay lady
    And there he did her burn.

WITCHES' CHARMS

I

Dame, dame! the watch is set
Quickly come, we all are met.
From the lakes and from the fens,
From the rocks and from the dens,
From the woods and from the caves,
From the churchyards, from the graves,
From the dungeon, from the tree
That they die on, here are we!

2

The weather is fair, the wind is good
Up, dame, on your horse of wood!
Or else tuck up your grey frock,
And saddle your goat or your green cock,
And make his bridle a ball of thread
To roll up how many miles you have rid.
Quickly come away,
For we all stay.

3

The owl is abroad, the bat and the toad,
   And so is the cat-a-mountain;*
The ant and the mole sit both in a hole,
   And the frog peeps out of the fountain,
The dogs they do bay, and the timbrels† play.
   The spindle is now a-turning;
The moon it is red, and the stars are fled,
   But the sky is a-burning.

BEN JONSON

* Wild cat. † Tambourines.

THE WOODS AND BANKS

The woods and banks of England now,
   Late coppered with dead leaves and old,
Have made the early violets grow,
   And bulge with knots of primrose gold.
Hear how the blackbird flutes away,
   Whose music scorns to sleep at night:
Hear how the cuckoo shouts all day
   For echoes – to the world's delight:
Hallo, you imp of wonder, you –
Where are you now, cuckoo? Cuckoo!

W. H. DAVIES

WRITTEN IN MARCH

The cock is crowing,
The stream is flowing,
The small birds twitter,
The lake doth glitter,
The green field sleeps in the sun;
The oldest and youngest
Are at work with the strongest;
The cattle are grazing,
Their heads never raising;
There are forty feeding like one!

Like an army defeated
The snow hath retreated,
And now doth fare ill
On the top of the bare hill;
The ploughboy is whooping – anon – anon:
There's joy in the mountains;
There's life in the fountains;
Small clouds are sailing,
Blue sky prevailing;
The rain is over and gone!

WILLIAM WORDSWORTH

A YANKEE SHIP

A Yankee ship came down the river,
Blow, boys, blow.
Her masts and yards they shine like silver.
Blow, my bully boys, blow.

And how d'ye know she's a Yankee packet?
Blow, boys, blow,
The Stars and Stripes they fly above her.
Blow, my bully boys, blow.

And who d'ye think was skipper of her?
Blow, boys, blow.
And who d'ye think was skipper of her?
Blow, my bully boys, blow.

'Twas Dandy Jim, the one-eyed nigger;
Blow, boys, blow.
'Twas Dandy Jim, with his bully figure.
Blow, my bully boys, blow.

And what d'ye think they had for dinner?
Blow, boys, blow.
Why bullock's lights and donkey's liver.
Blow, my bully boys, blow.

And what d'ye think they had for supper?
Blow, boys, blow.
Why weevilled bread and Yankee leather.
Blow, my bully boys, blow.

Then blow my boys and blow together.
Blow, blow, blow.
And blow my boys for better weather.
Blow, my bully boys, blow.

YORK, YORK, FOR MY MONEY

As I went through the North country,
The fashions of the world to see,
I sought for merry company
    To go to the City of London.
And when to the City of York I came,
I found good company in the same,
As well disposed to every game
    As if it had been at London.

York, York, for my money;
Of all the cities that ever I see
For merry pastime and company,
    Except the City of London.

And in that City what saw I then?
Knights and Squires and gentlemen
A shooting went for matches ten,
     As if it had been at London.
And they shot for twenty pounds a bow,
Besides great cheer they did bestow,
I never saw a gallanter show,
     Except I had been at London.

York, York for my money;
Of all the cities that ever I see
For merry pastime and company
     Except the City of London.

WILLIAM ELDERTON

(Verses from a ballad sung to the tune of *Greensleeves*)

YOU ARE OLD, FATHER WILLIAM

'You are old, Father William,' the young man said,
     'And your hair has become very white;
And yet you incessantly stand on your head -
     Do you think, at your age, it is right?'

'In my youth,' Father William replied to his son,
     'I feared it might injure the brain;
But now that I'm perfectly sure I have none,
     Why, I do it again and again.'

'You are old,' said the youth, 'as I mentioned before,
     And have grown most uncommonly fat;
Yet you turned a back-somersault in at the door —
     Pray, what is the reason of that?'

278

'In my youth,' said the sage, as he shook his grey locks,
  'I kept all my limbs very supple
By the use of this ointment – one shilling the box —
  Allow me to sell you a couple.'

'You are old,' said the youth, 'and your jaws are too weak
  For anything tougher than suet;
Yet you finished the goose, with the bones and the beak —
  Pray, how did you manage to do it?'

'In my youth,' said his father, 'I took to the law,
  And argued each case with my wife;
And the muscular strength which it gave to my jaw
  Has lasted the rest of my life.'

'You are old,' said the youth; 'one would hardly suppose
  That your eye was as steady as ever;
Yet you balanced an eel on the end of your nose —
  What made you so awfully clever?'

'I have answered three questions, and that is enough,'
  Said his father; 'don't give yourself airs!
Do you think I can listen all day to such stuff?
  Be off, or I'll kick you down stairs!'

LEWIS CARROLL

YOU SPOTTED SNAKES

FIRST FAIRY
You spotted snakes with double tongue,
  Thorny hedgehogs, be not seen;
Newts and blind-worms, do no wrong,
  Come not near our fairy queen.

CHORUS
Philomel, with melody
   Sing in our sweet lullaby;
Lulla, lulla, lullaby;
Lulla, lulla, lullaby:
     Never harm,
   Nor spell nor charm,
   Come our lovely lady nigh;
   So, good night, with lullaby.

SECOND FAIRY
Weaving spiders, come not here;
   Hence, you long-legged spinners hence!
Beetles black, approach not near;
   Worm nor snail, do no offence.

CHORUS
Philomel, with melody . . .

FIRST FAIRY
Hence, away! now all is well;
One aloof stand sentinel.

WILLIAM SHAKESPEARE

INDEX OF TITLES AND
FIRST LINES

285

INDEX OF AUTHORS

THE PUFFIN BOOK OF NURSERY RHYMES
Peter and Iona Opie

The first comprehensive collection of nursery rhymes to be produced as a paperback, prepared for Puffins by the leading authorities on children's lore. 220 pages, exquisitely illustrated on every page by Pauline Baynes.

FOUR FEET AND TWO
compiled by Leila Berg

The poems in this anthology have been chosen for the simplicity and directness of approach which is so much part of a child's own vision. The idea running through it is man's part in the whole of creation, sharing the earth in equal partnership with all living things, even to the snake in the grass and the fly on the window-pane. The selection is fresh and unusual; most people will find in it something new to them.

SELECTED CAUTIONARY VERSES
Hilaire Belloc

This revised collection of the best of Belloc contains a number of his superbly funny cautionary tales in verse and some useful observations on animal behaviour.

THE YOUNG PUFFIN BOOK OF VERSE
compiled by Barbara Ireson

This is a collection of poems, verses, nursery rhymes and jingles for children up to the age of eight. It is an introduction to a vast heritage of poetry. Though diverse in form, language, mood and subject, each poem has been chosen with care as being within the grasp of young readers and listeners.

There are poems included by writers whose names are by-words in the world of children's literature: Edward Lear, Kate Greenaway and Walter de la Mare, as well as many poems by writers whose names are normally found only in collections for adults: Robert Frost, W. B. Yeats, James Kirkup. All the poets with whom modern children are familiar are here too, including James Reeves, Rachel Field, Eleanor Farjeon and Leonard Clark. Finally, there are also many anonymous poems.

A PUFFIN BOOK OF VERSE

Compiled by Eleanor Graham

This anthology is intended simply to give pleasure, and it is hoped that every boy or girl who browses among its pages will find something to enjoy.

It ranges from nursery rhymes and nonsense poems to verses whose meaning has to be thought about: but whether the poems are simple or more difficult, they have been chosen partly for that beauty of rhythm and language which makes lines linger in the mind after the book that contains them has been put aside.

A PUFFIN QUARTET OF POETS

Edited by Eleanor Graham

This unusual anthology contains a selection of poems from the work of only four poets, but four of the finest who are writing verse for children today. A substantial amount from the work of each is given, enough to show their individual quality and special characteristics. The quartet is made up of Eleanor Farjeon, James Reeves, E. V. Rieu, and Ian Serraillier.

A CHILD'S GARDEN OF VERSES

Robert Louis Stevenson

There are more than sixty famous verses by Robert Louis Stevenson in this book, and they are illustrated with many drawings by Eve Garnett. 'These are rhymes, jingles,' the author wrote to a friend. 'I don't go in for eternity and the three unities.' They are rhymes about his childhood, divided into three sections – *The Child Alone*, *Garden Days* and *Envoys*.